THEORY OF FUNCTIONS

PART TWO

THEORY OF FUNCTIONS

By

DR. KONRAD KNOPP

Professor of Mathematics at the University of Tübingen

Translated by

FREDERICK BAGEMIHL, M. A.

Instructor in Mathematics at the University of Rochester

PART TWO

APPLICATIONS AND CONTINUATION OF THE GENERAL THEORY

NEW YORK

DOVER PUBLICATIONS

First American Edition

Translated From the
Fourth German Edition

Library of Congress Catalog Card Number: 45-6381

Manufactured in the United States of America

Dover Publications, Inc.
180 Varick Street
New York 14, N. Y.

CONTENTS

Section II

Multiple-valued Functions

INTRODUCTION

The foundations of the general theory of analytic functions were laid in Part I of this *Theory of Functions*.[1] Special functions (such as e^z, $\sin z$, $\log z$, $\sqrt[p]{z}$, and others) or classes of functions (such as the rational or the entire functions) were dealt with there only occasionally. Now such more detailed investigations will come in greater measure to the foreground. Only once again, later on, will more general considerations be carried out, in order to clarify the situation left undiscussed in I, §24, pp. 103-104. In doing so, it will become apparent that the distinction between single-valued and multiple-valued functions which was indicated there is quite fundamental. This distinction will therefore serve from the outset as a standard for all of the following presentation.

From these two main classes we shall select several especially characteristic and important types of functions. A certain arbitrariness is unavoidable in this connection, since completeness within the close compass of this little book is naturally denied us. We shall get away from this danger most easily if we start with the elementary functions (the entire and fractional rational functions, e^z, $\sin z$, $\log z$, $\sqrt[p]{z}$, $\cdots$) as the most

[1]*Theory of Functions, Part I: Elements of the General Theory of Analytic Functions*, translated from the 5th German edition, New York, 1945,—referred to in the following, briefly, as "I", together with paragraph or page number.

important ones, and try to understand that which is essential and of a universal character in their principal properties.[1]

The *entire rational functions* (*polynomials*)—evidently the simplest and most transparent functions—are characterized (cf. I, p. 137) "purely function-theoretically" by the fact that they are regular in the entire plane and have a pole at the point ∞. If one ignores the last property, one arrives at the more general class of *entire functions*, which are characterized solely by the property of being regular in the entire plane (excluding ∞), and to which the entire rational and the entire transcendental functions belong as special cases. They also appeared to us in I, §27 to be the simplest, because their power-series expansion for an arbitrary center converges, and therefore represents the function, in the entire plane. Since analytic continuation, then, is out of the question, the entire functions are naturally single-valued. In their totality they are identical with the totality of everywhere-convergent power series of the form

$$g(z) = \sum_{n=0}^{\infty} a_n z^n,$$

and, as such, appear to be an immediate generalization of the entire rational functions.

[1]Thus, we can be concerned in the following with a selection only—with samples, so to speak. The theory of functions is a large realm, which cannot be explored on a journey of one or even several days. If, in spite of this, we undertake on the following pages to sketch briefly a few of the principal places in this realm, we must emphatically caution the reader not to identify the extent of this little volume with that of the theory of functions.

In the first chapter we shall approach these functions with the question: Which of the fundamental properties of the entire rational functions does the class of entire functions still possess, and which not?—and shall give several answers to this question.

According to I, §35, Theorems 1 and 2, the *fractional rational functions* are completely characterized from the purely function-theoretical point of view by the fact that they have no singularities other than poles in the entire plane and at the point ∞. If, here too, one ignores the last property concerning the point ∞, one arrives again at a more general class of functions, the so-called *meromorphic functions*, which are characterized solely by the property of having no singularities other than poles in the entire plane (excluding ∞).

In the second chapter we shall approach these functions, which will also prove to be single-valued, with the question to be formulated analogous to the one above.

The property of the functions e^z, $\sin z$, and others, which is the most interesting from the function-theoretical standpoint, is their periodicity. In the third chapter we shall detach this property from the special nature of these functions, and investigate it more closely and purely function-theoretically. We thus arrive at the classes of *simply periodic* and *doubly periodic functions*. In the latter class we then meet, in particular, the *elliptic functions*.

These types chosen from the realm of single-valued functions will have to suffice.

In connection with *multiple-valued functions*, we shall first be concerned with sifting out the concept of the same more clearly than was possible in I, §24, and with giving a clearer notion of the essence of multiple-valuedness. This is accomplished in the fourth chapter by means of a very simple and, just for this reason, remarkably ingenious idea, that of the so-called *Riemann surface*. The construction of these surfaces is illustrated using the simplest multiple-valued functions,

$$\sqrt[p]{z}, \log z, \sqrt{(z - a_1)(z - a_2) \cdots (z - a_k)}.$$

In the fifth chapter, a particularly important and therefore also especially well-investigated class of multiple-valued functions, the class of *algebraic functions*, is treated in somewhat greater detail.

With the aid of the concept of the *algebraic singularity* acquired hereby, all gaps still contained in our definition of the complete analytic function or of the analytic configuration, given in I, pp.102-103, are finally filled in chapter 6. Thus is obtained in its complete generality the notion of the *analytic configuration*. This admirable concept, occupying the center of our considerations from the very beginning, though by no means to be mastered in the first attack, is undisputedly one of the most profound and beautiful in all of mathematical science.

SECTION I

SINGLE-VALUED FUNCTIONS

CHAPTER 1

ENTIRE FUNCTIONS

§1. Weierstrass's Factor-Theorem

The most important property of the entire rational functions is expressed in the fundamental theorem of algebra (see I, pp.113 and 139): *Every non-constant entire rational function has zeros.* Since e^z, for example, has no zeros (because $e^z \cdot e^{-z} = 1$), the question formulated above seems immediately doomed to unfruitfulness. Upon further investigation of the core of the matter, however, we shall see that this is not so. Indeed, if

$$g_0(z) = a_0 + a_1 z + \cdots + a_m z^m,$$

$$(m \geq 1,\ a_m \neq 0)$$

is an arbitrary, non-constant entire rational function, then it follows from the fundamental theorem of algebra that $g_0(z)$ can be written in the form

$$(1) \qquad g_0(z) = a_m(z - z_1)^{\alpha_1}(z - z_2)^{\alpha_2} \cdots (z - z_k)^{\alpha_k},$$

where $z_1, z_2, \cdots, z_k$ denote all the distinct zeros of $g_0(z)$, and $\alpha_1, \alpha_2, \cdots, \alpha_k$ denote their respective orders. We express this as follows:

(A) For every entire rational function there is a

so-called *factor representation*, which displays its zeros as to position and order.[1]

We infer immediately from this representation, that every other entire rational function $g(z)$ which has the same zeros to the same respective orders can differ from $g_0(z)$ only in the factor a_m. Furthermore, one can give these zeros any position and any order. In other words:

(B) It is always possible to construct an entire rational function whose zeros (finite in number, of course) are prescribed as to position and order. This function can be represented as a *product* which displays these zeros. The most general function of this kind is obtained from a particular one by multiplying it by an arbitrary non-zero factor ("a multiplicative entire rational function with no zeros").

If we take these two statements (A) and (B) to express the content of the fundamental theorem of algebra, then we shall see that all this can be carried over word for word to arbitrary entire functions.

To this end, we begin by setting ourselves the following **problem,** which corresponds to (B) and is fundamental for all that follows. We propose to investigate whether, and how, one can construct entire functions with prescribed zeros,[2] and to what extent an entire function is determined by these conditions.

[1]This also holds for entire rational functions "with no zeros", i.e., of degree zero (namely, the non-zero constants), for which the factor representation consists of the factor $a_m (= a_0 \neq 0)$ alone. On the other hand, our considerations, of course, no longer apply to the constant 0.

[2]This means that the function is to have zeros of certain prescribed orders at certain prescribed points, *and be distinct from zero at all other points.*

Entire functions with no zeros. Suppose the entire function to be constructed is to have no zeros at all. Then the constant 1, or the function e^z, or e^{z^2}, or, more generally, $e^{h(z)}$ is a solution of the problem, if $h(z)$ is a completely arbitrary *entire* function. The last answer is also the *most general* solution of the problem. That is, $e^{h(z)}$ (with $h(z)$ an arbitrary entire function) is not only always an entire function with no zeros, but conversely, every such function can be written in the form $e^{h(z)}$. We state this more briefly:

Theorem 1. *If $h(z)$ denotes an arbitrary entire function, then $e^{h(z)}$ is the most general entire function with no zeros.*[1]

Proof: We have only to show that if $H(z) = a_0 + a_1z + a_2z^2 + a_3z^3 + \cdots$ is a given entire function with no zeros, another entire function $h(z) = b_0 + b_1z + \cdots$ can be determined such that $e^{h(z)} = H(z)$. Now, since $H(z) \neq 0$, we have in particular $a_0 = H(0) \neq 0$. Hence, b_0 can be chosen such that $e^{b_0} = a_0$; for, e^z takes on every value except zero. Likewise, $\dfrac{1}{H(z)}$ is everywhere single-valued and regular, and is therefore

[1]This theorem seems almost trivial if we make use of the multiple-valued function log. For, let $H(z)$ be an entire function which is nowhere equal to zero. Then $h(z) = \log H(z)$, with the condition that, e.g., $h(0)$ be the principal value of $\log H(0)$, is also a regular function of z in a certain neighborhood of the origin. Its expansion there, $h(z) = b_0 + b_1z + b_2z^2 + \cdots$, consequently has a positive radius of convergence. This must (by I, §24, Theorem 1) be $+\infty$; because $\log H(z)$ can be singular only where $H(z)$ is singular or equal to zero, and hence, nowhere in the finite part of the plane.

an entire function. The same is true of $H'(z)$, so that

$$\frac{H'(z)}{H(z)} = c_0 + c_1 z + c_2 z^2 + \cdots$$

is also an entire function, and this series is everywhere convergent. The latter also holds for the series

$$b_0 + c_0 z + \frac{c_1}{2} z^2 + \cdots + \frac{c_{n-1}}{n} z^n + \cdots$$

$$= b_0 + b_1 z + \cdots + b_n z^n + \cdots,$$

which accordingly represents an entire function, $h(z)$. If we set $e^{h(z)} = H_1(z)$, then

$$\frac{H_1'(z)}{H_1(z)} = c_0 + c_1 z + c_2 z^2 + \cdots = \frac{H'(z)}{H(z)},$$

and hence $H_1 \cdot H' - H \cdot H_1' = 0$. Consequently

$$\frac{H \cdot H_1' - H_1 \cdot H'}{H^2} = \frac{d}{dz}\left(\frac{H_1(z)}{H(z)}\right) = 0,$$

and the quotient of the two functions $H_1(z)$ and $H(z)$ is constant. For $z = 0$ we find the value 1 for this constant. Therefore

$$H(z) = H_1(z) = e^{h(z)}, \qquad \text{Q. E. D.}[1]$$

Having thus completely solved our problem for the case that *no* zeros are prescribed, it is easy to see the

[1]The proof actually demonstrates the following: If two functions $f(z)$ and $f_1(z)$ are *single-valued regular, and distinct from zero* in a region $\mathfrak{G}$, and if their logarithmic derivatives f'/f and f_1'/f_1 coincide there, then they differ in $\mathfrak{G}$ by at most a constant factor (which must, of course, be equal to unity if f and f_1 have the same value at some point of $\mathfrak{G}$).

extent to which an entire function in general is determined by its zeros. If $G_0(z)$ and $G(z)$ are two entire functions which coincide in the positions and orders of their zeros, then (cf. I, §21, Theorem 4) their quotient is also an entire function, but one with *no* zeros. $G(z)$ and $G_0(z)$ thus differ (cf. statement (B)) by at most a multiplicative entire function with no zeros. Conversely, the presence of such a factor of $G_0(z)$ does not alter the positions or orders of its zeros. In connection with Theorem 1, we express this as follows:

Theorem 2. *Let $G_0(z)$ be a particular entire function. Then, if $h(z)$ denotes an arbitrary entire function,*

$$G(z) = e^{h(z)} \cdot G_0(z)$$

is the most general entire function whose zeros coincide with those of $G_0(z)$ in position and order.

The question of the possibility and method of constructing a particular entire function with arbitrarily prescribed zeros now remains to be settled.

We must begin by restricting our requirements. An entire function has no singularity in the finite part of the plane; therefore, according to I, §21, Theorem 1, it can have only a finite number of zeros in every finite region. The prescribed points consequently must not have a finite limit point. If we make this single restriction, which is in the nature of things, we shall see that an entire function of the kind in question can always be constructed. It will be possible to set it up in the form of a product (analogous to the case of the entire rational functions; cf. (1)) which exhibits the positions and orders of its zeros. We have indeed the following theorem, which is named after its discoverer:

Weierstrass's factor-theorem. *Let any finite or infinite set of points having no finite limit point be prescribed, and associate with each of its points a definite positive integer as order. Then there exists an entire function which has zeros to the prescribed orders at precisely the prescribed points, and is otherwise different from zero. It can be represented as a product (see p. 18 for the final form) from which one can read off again the positions and orders of the zeros. Further, by Theorem 2, if $G_0(z)$ is one such function,*

$$G(z) = e^{h(z)} \cdot G_0(z)$$

is the most general function satisfying the conditions of the problem, if $h(z)$ denotes an arbitrary entire function.[1]

If we regard this fundamental theorem for the moment as having been proved, it follows immediately therefrom, that the first of our two statements concerning the entire rational functions can also be carried over to arbitrary entire functions. For, let $G(z)$ be an arbitrarily given entire function. Then the set of its zeros has no finite limit point. Hence, according to Weierstrass's theorem, another entire function $G_0(z)$, having precisely the same zeros in position and order, can be constructed in the form of a product displaying these. Then, by Theorem 2,

$$G(z) = e^{h_0(z)} \cdot G_0(z),$$

[1]If the entire function to be constructed is to have no zeros, then the factor $G_0(z)$ is to be suppressed, i.e., replaced by unity, which is nevertheless an entire function with the prescribed zeros.

where $h_0(z)$ denotes a suitable entire function. We have thus actually obtained a *factor representation* of the given entire function $G(z)$, from which the positions and orders of its zeros can be read off.

The two statements (A) and (B) concerning entire rational functions have herewith been carried over verbatim to arbitrary entire functions.

The next paragraph is devoted to a proof of Weierstrass's factor-theorem.

Exercises. 1. $\dfrac{\sin iz}{e^{2z} - 1}$ is an entire function with no zeros. (Proof?) Hence, according to Theorem 1, it can be expressed in the form $e^{h(z)}$. How should $h(z)$ be chosen?

2. $\cos iz$ and $e^{2z} + 1$ have the same zeros in position and order. (Proof?) By Theorem 2, the second function can be obtained from the first by multiplying it by a suitable factor of the form $e^{h(z)}$. How should $h(z)$ be chosen?

§2. Proof of Weierstrass's Factor-theorem

As we have already pointed out, the entire function satisfying the conditions of Weierstrass's factor-theorem will be set up in the form of a product; in general, in the form of an infinite product. As with infinite series, we shall assume that the simplest facts in the theory of infinite products with constant factors are familiar to the reader.

Since, however, these are not so universally well-known, and in order to provide a firm foundation for what follows, we present very briefly, without proofs, the most important definitions and theorems for our purposes.[1]

Definition. *The infinite product*

$$(1) \qquad u_1 \cdot u_2 \cdots u_\nu \cdots = \prod_{\nu=1}^{\infty} u_\nu,$$

in which the factors are arbitrary complex numbers, is said to be **convergent** *(in the stricter sense) if, and only if, from a certain index on, say for all* $\nu > m$*, no factor vanishes, and*

$$\lim_{n\to\infty} (u_{m+1} \cdot u_{m+2} \cdots u_n)$$

exists and has a finite value distinct from zero. If we call this limit U_m*, then the number*

$$U = u_1 \cdot u_2 \cdots u_m \cdot U_m,$$

which is obviously independent of m*, is regarded as the* **value** *of the infinite product* (1).[2]

[1]Detailed proofs are given in K. Knopp, *Theory and Application of Infinite Series*, translated by R. C. Young, London and Glasgow, 1928.

[2]With reference to the corresponding definition for infinite series, one might already be inclined to call the product (1) convergent with the value U if

$$\lim_{n\to\infty} (u_1 \cdot u_2 \cdots u_n) = U.$$

But then *every* product in which only a *single* factor vanishes would evidently be convergent, and *always* with the same value zero. Likewise, *every* product such that $|u_\nu| \leq \theta < 1$ for all $\nu > m$ would be convergent, and *always* with the same value zero. To exclude these cases we employ the more useful definition above, and, if necessary, draw attention to the restriction it contains by adding: "in the stricter sense".

The following theorems are easily proved for such convergent infinite products:

Theorem 1. *A convergent product has the value zero if, and only if, one of its factors vanishes.*

Theorem 2. *The infinite product* (1) *is convergent if, and only if, having chosen an arbitrary* $\epsilon > 0$, *an index* n_0 *can be determined such that*

$$|u_{n+1} \cdot u_{n+2} \cdots u_{n+r} - 1| < \epsilon$$

for all $n > n_0$ *and all* $r \geq 1$ (cf. I, §3, Theorem 4).

Since on the basis of this theorem (let $r = 1$ and $n + 1 = \nu$) it is necessary that $\lim_{\nu \to \infty} u_\nu = 1$, one usually sets the factors of the product equal to $1 + c_\nu$, so that instead of dealing with (1) one is concerned with products of the form

$$\prod_{\nu=1}^{\infty} (1 + c_\nu). \tag{2}$$

For these, then, $c_\nu \to 0$ is a necessary (*but by no means sufficient*) condition for convergence.

We make use of the following

Definition. *The product* (2) *is said to be absolutely convergent if*

$$\prod_{\nu=1}^{\infty} (1 + |c_\nu|)$$

converges.[1]

[1]The definition which first suggests itself: "Πu_ν shall be called absolutely convergent if $\Pi |u_\nu|$ converges," is not to the purpose, since then *every* convergent product would at the same time converge absolutely.

We then have

Theorem 3. *Absolute convergence is a sufficient condition for ordinary convergence; in other words, the convergence of* $\Pi(1 + |c_\nu|)$ *implies that of* $\Pi(1 + c_\nu)$.

On the basis of this theorem it will be sufficient for our purposes to have convergence criteria for absolutely convergent products. The following two theorems settle completely the question of convergence for these products:

Theorem 4. *The product* $\Pi(1 + \gamma_\nu)$, *with* $\gamma_\nu \geq 0$, *is convergent if, and only if, the series* $\Sigma\gamma_\nu$ *converges.*

Theorem 5. *For* $\Pi(1 + c_\nu)$ *to converge absolutely, it is necessary and sufficient that* Σc_ν *converge absolutely.*[1]

The following theorem is analogous to one on absolutely convergent series:

Theorem 6. *If the order in which the factors of an absolutely convergent product occur is changed in a completely arbitrary manner, the product remains convergent and has the same value.*[2]

[1]According to this, $\prod_{\nu=1}^{\infty}(1 - (z^2/\nu^2))$, for example, is absolutely convergent for every value of z, because the series $\Sigma|z^2/\nu^2| = |z|^2\,\Sigma(1/\nu^2)$ converges.

[2]In other words, the *commutative law* holds for absolutely convergent infinite products as well as for products having only a finite number of factors. This is not true for non-absolutely convergent products. On the other hand, the *associative law* holds for all convergent products, i.e., one may, in an arbitrary manner, group consecutive factors into one by means of parentheses.

In addition to products with constant factors, we need products whose factors are functions of a complex variable z. We shall write these products in the form

$$(3) \qquad \prod_{\nu=1}^{\infty} (1 + f_\nu(z)).$$

Analogous to the considerations in I, ch. 6, we designate as the *region of convergence* of such a product the set $\mathfrak{M}$ of all those points z which (a) belong to the domain of definition of *every* $f_\nu(z)$, and for which (b) the product (3) is convergent.[1] According to this, the product furnishes a certain value for every z of $\mathfrak{M}$; we say, therefore, that the product represents in $\mathfrak{M}$ a certain (single-valued) function. For our function-theoretical purposes, it is again (cf. I, §19, Theorem 3) particularly important to possess useful conditions under which such a product, in its region of convergence, represents an *analytic function.* The following theorem is adequate:

Theorem 7. *Let $f_1(z), f_2(z), \cdots, f_\nu(z), \cdots$ be an infinite sequence of functions, and suppose a region $\mathfrak{G}$ exists in which all these functions are regular. Let $\sum_{\nu=1}^{\infty} | f_\nu(z) |$ be uniformly convergent in every closed subregion $\mathfrak{G}'$ of $\mathfrak{G}$ (cf. I, p. 74). Then the product (3) is convergent in the entire region $\mathfrak{G}$, and represents a regular function $f(z)$ in $\mathfrak{G}$. Moreover, this function, by Theorem 1, has a zero at those, and only those, points of $\mathfrak{G}$ at which at least one*

[1]For instance, the region of convergence of $\prod_{\nu=1}^{\infty} (1 - (z^2/\nu^2))$ is the entire z-plane, according to the last footnote but one.

of the factors is equal to zero. The order of such a zero is equal to the sum of the orders to which these factors[1] *vanish there.*

Proof: Let $\mathfrak{G}'$ be an arbitrary closed subregion of $\mathfrak{G}$. For every $m \geq 0$,

$$\sum_{\nu=m+1}^{\infty} | f_\nu(z) | , \text{ along with } \sum_{\nu=1}^{\infty} | f_\nu(z) | ,$$

converges uniformly in $\mathfrak{G}'$. By Theorem 5, the product

$$\prod_{\nu=m+1}^{\infty} (1 + f_\nu(z)) \tag{4}$$

is absolutely convergent in $\mathfrak{G}'$, and represents a certain function there. Let us call this function $F_m(z)$. Now, choose the number m such that

$$| f_{n+1}(z) | + | f_{n+2}(z) | + \cdots + | f_{n+r}(z) | < \tfrac{1}{2} \tag{5}$$

for all $n \geq m$, all $r \geq 1$, and all z in $\mathfrak{G}'$ (this is possible by I, §18). Then $F_m(z)$ is actually regular and distinct from zero in $\mathfrak{G}'$. Indeed, if, for $n > m$, we set

$$\prod_{\nu=m+1}^{n} (1 + f_\nu(z)) = P_n \quad \text{and} \quad P_m = 0$$

for abbreviation, we have

$$F_m(z) = \lim_{n\to\infty} P_n$$

$$= \lim_{n\to\infty} [(P_{m+1}-P_m)+(P_{m+2}-P_{m+1})+\cdots+(P_n-P_{n-1})],$$

[1]The proof will show that there are only a finite number of factors in question.

or

$$(6) \qquad F_m(z) = \sum_{\nu=m+1}^{\infty} (P_\nu - P_{\nu-1}),$$

and $F_m(z)$ is thus represented by an infinite series. Now the theorems of I, §19 bring us rapidly to our goal. Since, for $n > m$,

$$|P_n| \leq (1 + |f_{m+1}(z)|) \cdots (1 + |f_n(z)|)$$
$$\leq e^{|f_{m+1}(z)| + \cdots + |f_n(z)|} < e^{\frac{1}{2}} < 2,\text{[1]}$$

the inequality

$$|P_\nu - P_{\nu-1}| = |P_{\nu-1}| \cdot |f_\nu(z)| < 2 \, |f_\nu(z)|$$

is valid for the terms (from the second onward) of the series just obtained. Consequently, the new series (6), along with $\Sigma \, |f_\nu(z)|$, is uniformly convergent in $\mathfrak{G}'$, and the function $F_m(z)$ defined by that series is a regular function in $\mathfrak{G}'$. It is also distinct from zero there. For, by (5), we have in $\mathfrak{G}'$, for $n \geq m$,

$$|f_{n+1}(z)| < \tfrac{1}{2},$$

and hence, for $\nu \geq m + 1$,

$$|1 + f_\nu(z)| \geq 1 - |f_\nu(z)| > \tfrac{1}{2},$$

so that no factor of F_m can be equal to zero. Since

$$f(z) = (1 + f_1(z)) \cdots (1 + f_m(z)) \cdot F_m(z),$$

$f(z)$, together with $F_m(z)$, is regular at every point z of $\mathfrak{G}'$, and can vanish at such a point only if one of the

[1]For $x \geq 0$, $1 + x \leq 1 + x + x^2/2! + \cdots = e^x$.

factors appearing before $F_m(z)$ vanishes. The order of such a zero is then indeed equal to the sum of the orders to which these factors vanish there.

Now let z be an arbitrary point of $\mathfrak{G}$. Since z is *eo ipso* an *interior* point of $\mathfrak{G}$, it is always possible to choose $\mathfrak{G}'$ such that z also belongs to $\mathfrak{G}'$. Hence, the above considerations are valid for the entire region $\mathfrak{G}$, and the proof of the theorem is complete.

Corresponding to the further content of Theorem 3 in I, §19, it is also possible to make an assertion concerning the derivative of $f(z)$. Since the ordinary derivative of a product of many factors is difficult to survey, however, it is more advantageous to choose the so-called logarithmic derivative[1] for this purpose.

We then have the following theorem concerning this derivative:

Theorem 8. *Under the hypotheses of Theorem 7,*

$$\frac{f'(z)}{f(z)} = \sum_{\nu=1}^{\infty} \frac{f'_\nu(z)}{1 + f_\nu(z)} \tag{7}$$

for every point z of $\mathfrak{G}$ at which $f(z) \neq 0$; i.e., the series on the right is convergent for every such z and furnishes the logarithmic derivative of $f(z)$.

Proof: If z is a particular point of the type mentioned, and if the subregion $\mathfrak{G}'$ is chosen so as to contain z, then

[1]This is defined as the ordinary derivative divided by the original function. If $F(z) = g_1(z) \cdot g_2(z) \cdots g_k(z)$, and if all the factors are differentiable and distinct from zero at z_0, then

$$\frac{F'(z_0)}{F(z_0)} = \frac{g'_1(z_0)}{g_1(z_0)} + \frac{g'_2(z_0)}{g_2(z_0)} + \cdots + \frac{g'_k(z_0)}{g_k(z_0)}.$$

$$(8)\quad \frac{f'(z)}{f(z)} = \frac{f_1'(z)}{1 + f_1(z)} + \cdots + \frac{f_m'(z)}{1 + f_m(z)} + \frac{F_m'(z)}{F_m(z)}.$$

Since the series (6) converges uniformly in $\mathfrak{G}'$,

$$F_m'(z) = \sum_{\nu=m+1}^{\infty} (P_\nu' - P_{\nu-1}') = \lim_{n\to\infty} P_n',$$

according to I, §19, Theorem 3. Here P_n' denotes the derivative of P_n. Since $F_m(z)$ and all P_n for $n > m$ are not zero,

$$\frac{F_m'(z)}{F_m(z)} = \lim_{n\to\infty} \frac{P_n'}{P_n} = \lim_{n\to\infty}\left(\frac{f_{m+1}'(z)}{1 + f_{m+1}(z)} + \cdots + \frac{f_n'(z)}{1 + f_n(z)}\right)$$

$$= \sum_{\nu=m+1}^{\infty} \frac{f_\nu'(z)}{1 + f_\nu(z)},$$

which, with (8), proves the assertion.

Theorem 9. *The series (7) converges absolutely and uniformly in every closed subregion $\mathfrak{G}''$ of $\mathfrak{G}$ containing no zero of $f(z)$, and hence may be repeatedly differentiated there any number of times term by term.*

Proof: Since none of the factors $(1 + f_\nu(z))$ can vanish in $\mathfrak{G}''$, the absolute value of each remains greater than a positive bound[1], γ_ν say. Since this is certainly greater than $1/2$ for all $\nu > m$ (see above), a positive number γ exists, such that $\gamma_\nu \geq \gamma > 0$ for *all* ν. Then, for all ν and all z in $\mathfrak{G}''$,

$$\left| \frac{f_\nu'(z)}{1 + f_\nu(z)} \right| < \frac{1}{\gamma} \cdot | f_\nu'(z) |.$$

[1]For, $|1 + f_\nu(z)|$, as a continuous function, *attains* its greatest lower bound, and this cannot be zero in $\mathfrak{G}''$.

From the proof of Theorem 3 in I, §19 (cf. also Exercise 2 there) it follows that $\Sigma| f'_\nu(z) |$ converges uniformly in $\mathfrak{G}''$. By the last inequality, this is also true then of the series (7).

Having now familiarized ourselves to some extent with infinite products, it is an easy matter to prove Weierstrass's factor-theorem.

If only a *finite number* of points $z_1, z_2, \cdots, z_k$ with the respective orders $\alpha_1, \alpha_2, \cdots, \alpha_k$ are prescribed, then the product

$$(1) \qquad (z - z_1)^{\alpha_1} (z - z_2)^{\alpha_2} \cdots (z - z_k)^{\alpha_k}$$

is already a solution of the problem, so that this case is settled immediately. If, however, an *infinite number* of points are prescribed as zeros, we cannot proceed quite so simply, because the analogous product would be meaningless in general. This would still be the case if, with regard to the infinite products dealt with, we were to replace (1) by the product

$$(2) \qquad \left(1 - \frac{z}{z_1}\right)^{\alpha_1} \left(1 - \frac{z}{z_2}\right)^{\alpha_2} \cdots \left(1 - \frac{z}{z_k}\right)^{\alpha_k}$$

which serves the same purpose. We therefore proceed somewhat differently—and in this modification lies the originality of Weierstrass's method.

The set of prescribed points is enumerable (see I, p. 10), since every finite region can contain only a finite number of them. They can therefore be arranged in a sequence.[1] The way in which the points are numbered is

[1]This can be done, e.g., by describing circles about the origin with radii 1, 2, 3, $\cdots$, arranging the points as they appear in the consecutive circular rings, and ordering those (only finite in number) which lie in the same ring, according to any rule.

unimportant. However, if the origin, with the order α_0, is contained among them, we shall call this point z_0 and, leaving it aside for the present, arrange the remaining points in an arbitrary, but then fixed, sequence: $z_1, z_2, \cdots, z_\nu, \cdots$. Let the corresponding orders be $\alpha_1, \alpha_2, \cdots, \alpha_\nu, \cdots$. The z_ν are all different from zero; and since they have no finite limit point,

$$z_\nu \to \infty, \ |z_\nu| \to +\infty.$$

Consequently, it is possible (indeed, in many ways) to assign a sequence of positive integers $k_1, k_2, \cdots, k_\nu, \cdots$ such that

$$\sum_{\nu=1}^{\infty} \alpha_\nu \left(\frac{z}{z_\nu}\right)^{k_\nu} \tag{3}$$

is *absolutely* convergent for *every* z. In fact, it suffices, e.g.[1], to take $k_\nu = \nu + \alpha_\nu$. For, no matter what fixed value z mav have, since $z_\nu \to \infty$, we have for all sufficiently large ν

$$\left|\frac{z}{z_\nu}\right| < \tfrac{1}{2}$$

and hence

$$\left|\alpha_\nu \left(\frac{z}{z_\nu}\right)^{\nu+\alpha_\nu}\right| < \alpha_\nu \left(\tfrac{1}{2}\right)^{\nu+\alpha_\nu} < \left(\tfrac{1}{2}\right)^{\nu}, \ ^{2}$$

and the absolute convergence of the series is thus assured.

Let the numbers k_ν be chosen subject to this condi-

[1]Much smaller numbers will often do.

[2]$\alpha/2^\alpha < 1$ for every natural number α.

tion, but otherwise arbitrarily, and keep them fixed. Then we shall prove that the product[1]

$$G_0(z) = z^{\alpha_0} \cdot \prod_{\nu=1}^{\infty} \left[\left(1 - \frac{z}{z_\nu}\right) \cdot \exp\left\{ \frac{z}{z_\nu} + \frac{1}{2}\left(\frac{z}{z_\nu}\right)^2 + \cdots + \frac{1}{k_\nu - 1}\left(\frac{z}{z_\nu}\right)^{k_\nu - 1} \right\} \right]^{\alpha_\nu}$$

(Weierstrass's factor-theorem)

represents an entire function with the required properties[2]. (Here the factor z^{α_0} appearing before the product symbol is to be suppressed in case the origin is not one of the prescribed zeros (see above). Likewise, if one of the numbers k_ν is equal to unity, the corresponding exponential factor simply does not appear.)

The proof of this assertion is now very simple. To be able to apply our theorems on products, we set the factors of our infinite product equal to $1 + f_\nu(z)$. According to Theorem 7, we must then merely prove that

$$\sum_{\nu=1}^{\infty} |f_\nu(z)| = \sum_{\nu=1}^{\infty} \left| \left[\left(1 - \frac{z}{z_\nu}\right) \exp\left\{ \frac{z}{z_\nu} + \cdots + \frac{1}{k_\nu - 1}\left(\frac{z}{z_\nu}\right)^{k_\nu - 1} \right\} \right]^{\alpha_\nu} - 1 \right| \tag{4}$$

[1]We shall find it convenient sometimes to write exp z instead of e^z.

[2]The exponentials in the brackets ensure the convergence of the product, which would, in general, diverge without these. They are therefore called the *convergence-producing factors*.

Weierstrass called the expressions in the brackets *primary factors*.

converges uniformly in *every* bounded region. For then the entire plane can be taken as the region $\mathfrak{G}$ of Theorem 7, according to which the infinite product, and consequently also $G_0(z)$, is an entire function. On account of the form of the factors of $G_0(z)$, the second part of Theorem 7 at once yields that $G_0(z)$ also possesses the required properties. The uniform convergence of the series (4) in the circle about the origin with radius R ($R > 0$ arbitrary, but fixed) is established as follows:

Since the series (3) also converges for $z = R$, and since $z_\nu \to \infty$, m can be chosen so large that

$$\alpha_\nu \left| \frac{R}{z_\nu} \right|^{k_\nu} < \tfrac{1}{2} \quad \text{and} \quad \frac{R}{|z_\nu|} < \tfrac{1}{2} \tag{5}$$

for all $\nu > m$. Let us for the moment replace z/z_ν by u, k_ν by k, and α_ν by α. Then, for $v > m$, the νth term of the series (4) has the form

$$\left| \left[(1-u) \exp\left\{ u + \frac{u^2}{2} + \cdots + \frac{u^{k-1}}{k-1} \right\} \right]^\alpha - 1 \right|$$

with $\begin{cases} |u| < \frac{1}{2} \text{ and} \\ \alpha |u|^k < \frac{1}{2}. \end{cases}$

Now for $|u| < 1$ we can set[1]

$$1 - u = \exp\left\{ -u - \frac{u^2}{2} - \frac{u^3}{3} - \cdots \right\},$$

[1]For, the series in the exponent on the right has for its sum the principal value of $\log(1 - u)$.

According to the theorem formulated on p. 4, footnote, this simple fact also follows from the coincidence of both sides for $u = 0$ and the equality of their logarithmic derivatives for all $|u| < 1$.

so that this νth term is further equal to

$$\left| \exp\left\{\alpha\left(-\frac{u^k}{k} - \frac{u^{k+1}}{k+1} - \cdots\right)\right\} - 1 \right|,$$

and hence[1]

$$\leq \exp\left\{\alpha\left(\frac{|u|^k}{k} + \frac{|u|^{k+1}}{k+1} + \cdots\right)\right\} - 1$$

$$\leq \exp\left\{\alpha |u|^k(1 + |u| + |u|^2 + \cdots)\right\} - 1$$

$$< e^{2\alpha |u|^k} - 1,$$

because $|u| < \frac{1}{2}$. Further, since $e^x - 1 \leq xe^x$ for $x \geq 0$,[2] the νth term is less than or equal to

$$2\alpha |u|^k e^{2\alpha |u|^k} < 6\alpha |u|^k,$$

the exponent of e being smaller than one, according to (5). Hence, for all sufficiently large ν and all $|z| \leq R$ we have

$$|f_\nu(z)| < 6\alpha_\nu \left|\frac{z}{z_\nu}\right|^{k_\nu} \leq 6\alpha_\nu \left|\frac{R}{z_\nu}\right|^{k_\nu}.$$

But these are positive numbers whose sum converges (because of the manner in which the k_ν were chosen). Therefore, by Weierstrass's M-test, I, §18, $\Sigma |f_\nu(z)|$ is uniformly convergent in the circle with radius R about the origin as center, and so the proof of the Weierstrass factor-theorem is complete.

[1] $|e^w - 1| \leq |w| + |w^2/2!| + \cdots = e^{|w|} - 1$ for every complex number w.

[2] $e^x - 1 = x + x^2/2! + \cdots = x(1 + x/2! + x^2/3! + \cdots) \leq xe^x$.

Exercises. 1. Prove Theorems 1-6.

2. Establish the convergence of, and evaluate, each of the following products with constant factors:

$$\text{a)} \prod_{n=1}^{\infty}\left(1+\frac{1}{n(n+2)}\right); \qquad \text{b)} \prod_{n=2}^{\infty}\left(1-\frac{2}{n(n+1)}\right);$$

$$\text{c)} \prod_{n=2}^{\infty}\left(\frac{n^3-1}{n^3+1}\right).$$

3. Determine the region of convergence of each of the following products:

$$\text{a)} \prod_{n=1}^{\infty}(1-z^n); \quad \text{b)} \prod_{n=0}^{\infty}(1+z^{2^n}); \quad \text{c)} \prod_{n=2}^{\infty}\left(1-\frac{1}{n^z}\right);$$

d) $\prod_{p}\left(1-\frac{1}{p^z}\right)$, if p runs over all the prime numbers;

e) $\prod_{n=1}^{\infty}(1+c_n z)$, if Σc_n is an absolutely convergent series.

4. Prove the following formulas:

$$\text{a)} \prod_{p}\frac{1}{1-p^{-z}} = \sum_{n=1}^{\infty}\frac{1}{n^z} \text{ (cf. 3 c and d);}$$

$$\text{b)} \prod(1+z^{2^n}) = \frac{1}{1-z} \text{ (cf. 3 b).}$$

5. What values have the coefficients μ_n on the right-hand side in the equation

$$\prod_{p}\left(1-\frac{1}{p^z}\right) = \sum_{n=1}^{\infty}\frac{\mu_n}{n^z},$$

in which p again is to run over all the prime numbers.

6. If $z_1, z_2, \cdots, z_n, \cdots$ is any sequence of numbers which tends to ∞, then, if all $z_n \neq 0$,

$$\sum_{n=1}^{\infty} \left(\frac{z}{z_n}\right)^{\log n}$$

is convergent for every z. Hence, what smaller numbers k_ν can one always choose in the proof of Weierstrass's factor-theorem instead of the ones used in the text?

7. Prove the following transfer of Weierstrass's factor-theorem to the region of the unit circle:

Let $z_1, z_2, \cdots, z_n, \cdots$ be an arbitrary sequence of distinct points inside the unit circle, which have no limit point in the *interior* of this circle (but only on its circumference). Let $\alpha_1, \alpha_2, \cdots, \alpha_n, \cdots$ be a sequence of arbitrary positive integers. Then it is always possible to construct a function $f(z)$ (and indeed, in a form closely analogous to the Weierstrass product) which is regular in the unit circle, and there has zeros of the orders α_n at precisely the points z_n, respectively, (and no others).

8. With the aid of the preceding theorem, construct functions which have the unit circle for a natural boundary.

§3. Examples of Weierstrass's Factor-theorem

Since the formation of entire functions with prescribed zeros is extremely simple—it was only somewhat more laborious to carry out carefully all the proofs, —one can easily construct any number of examples.

The product is simplest if the prescribed zeros and orders are such, that the series $\sum \frac{\alpha_\nu}{z_\nu}$, and consequently, for every z, the series $\sum \alpha_\nu \left(\frac{z}{z_\nu}\right)$, converges absolutely for our sequence $z_1, z_2, \cdots$. For then it is possible to take all $k_\nu = 1$, and the desired function is obtained simply in the form

$$G_0(z) = z^{\alpha_0} \cdot \prod_{\nu=1}^{\infty} \left(1 - \frac{z}{z_\nu}\right)^{\alpha_\nu} .$$

If, e.g., the points $0, 1, 4, 9, \cdots, \nu^2, \cdots$ are to be zeros of order unity, then

$$G(z) = e^{h(z)} \cdot z \cdot \prod_{\nu=1}^{\infty} \left(1 - \frac{z}{\nu^2}\right),$$

with $h(z)$ an arbitrary entire function, is the most general solution of the problem. If the points $1, 8, \cdots, \nu^3, \cdots$ are to be zeros of respective orders $1, 2, \cdots, \nu, \cdots$, then

$$G(z) = e^{h(z)} \cdot \prod_{\nu=1}^{\infty} \left(1 - \frac{z}{\nu^3}\right)^{\nu}$$

is the most general solution.

In addition to these simple examples, whose number is easily enlarged, we shall now present several applications of the factor theorem which are of particular function-theoretical importance.

1st Example: sin πz. Consider the problem of constructing an entire function which has zeros, of order unity, at precisely all the real lattice points (i.e., at 0, $\pm 1, \pm 2, \cdots$). We number these points so that $z_0 = 0$, $z_1 = +1$, $z_2 = -1$, $\cdots$, $z_{2\nu-1} = \nu$, $z_{2\nu} = -\nu$, $\cdots$,

($\nu = 1, 2, \cdots$). The series

$$\sum_{\nu=1}^{\infty} \left(\frac{z}{z_\nu}\right)^2 = z^2 \cdot \sum_{\nu=1}^{\infty} \frac{1}{z_\nu^2}$$

is absolutely convergent for every z, and we can therefore take all $k_\nu = 2$. Then

$$G(z) = e^{h(z)} \cdot z \cdot \prod_{\nu=1}^{\infty} \left[\left(1 - \frac{z}{z_\nu}\right) e^{z/z_\nu}\right]$$

$$= e^{h(z)} \cdot z \cdot \prod_{\nu=1}^{\infty} \left[\left(1 - \frac{z}{\nu}\right) e^{z/\nu}\right]\left[\left(1 + \frac{z}{\nu}\right) e^{-z/\nu}\right]$$

$$= e^{h(z)} \cdot z \cdot \prod_{\nu=1}^{\infty} \left(1 - \frac{z^2}{\nu^2}\right)$$ [1]

is the most general solution of the problem.

Since the function $\sin \pi z$ is evidently also a solution of the problem, it must be contained in the expression just found. That is, there exists a certain entire function, which we shall call $h_0(z)$, such that

$$(1) \qquad \sin \pi z = e^{h_0(z)} \cdot z \cdot \prod_{\nu=1}^{\infty} \left(1 - \frac{z^2}{\nu^2}\right).$$

If we succeed in obtaining this function $h_0(z)$, we shall have the *factor representation* of $\sin \pi z$ in the sense of §1 (see p. 6).

The function $h_0(z)$ certainly can not be ascertained from a knowledge of the zeros *alone*. On the contrary, for its determination we must make use of further properties of the particular function $\sin \pi z$; e.g., its power-

[1]The transformations are justified according to p. 10, footnote 2.

series expansion, its periodicity properties, the conformal map effected by it, its behavior at infinity, etc. We sketch briefly a method for determining $h_0(z)$.[1]

First, we show that $h_0''(z)$ is a constant. According to §2, Theorem 8, it follows from (1) that

$$\text{(2)} \quad \pi \cot \pi z = h_0'(z) + \frac{1}{z} + \sum_{\nu=1}^{\infty} \left(\frac{1}{z-\nu} + \frac{1}{z+\nu} \right).$$

According to Theorem 9, this expression may be differentiated repeatedly term by term. Thus,

$$-\frac{\pi^2}{\sin^2 \pi z} = h_0''(z) - \frac{1}{z^2} - \sum_{\nu=1}^{\infty} \left(\frac{1}{(z-\nu)^2} + \frac{1}{(z+\nu)^2} \right),$$

or, written more briefly,

$$h_0''(z) = \sum_{\nu=-\infty}^{+\infty} \frac{1}{(z-\nu)^2} - \frac{\pi^2}{\sin^2 \pi z}.$$

This relation holds in every closed region which contains no real lattice points. If we replace z by $z + 1$ in the right-hand member, it is not altered; because $\sin^2 \pi z$ has the period $+1$, and

$$\sum_{\nu=-\infty}^{+\infty} \frac{1}{(z+1-\nu)^2} = \sum_{\nu=-\infty}^{+\infty} \frac{1}{(z-(\nu-1))^2} = \sum_{\mu=-\infty}^{+\infty} \frac{1}{(z-\mu)^2}.$$

[1]Here we are concerned with a *typical question*: One has two analytical expressions: $A_1(z)$ and $A_2(z)$, say, as in the present case the already familiar power-series representation of $\sin \pi z$ on the one hand, and the infinite product $z \cdot \Pi(1 - (z^2/\nu^2))$ on the other. In the course of an investigation, one is led to the conjecture that both expressions represent the same function, or stand in some simple relationship to one another. How can this be proved? The determination of $h_0(z)$ carried out in the text shows that even in the present apparently very simple instance such an identification is not very easily made.

Hence, $h_0''(z)$ is an entire function with the period $+1$. In order to show that $h_0''(z)$ is a constant, it is sufficient, by I, §28, 1, to show that $| h_0''(z) |$ cannot become arbitrarily large. On account of the periodicity of $h_0''(z)$ which we just established, it is sufficient, for this purpose, to show that a constant K exists such that $| h_0''(z) | < K$ for all $z = x + iy$ for which $0 \leq x \leq 1$ and $| y | \geq 1$.

Now for these z,

$$\left| \sum_{\nu=-\infty}^{+\infty} \frac{1}{(z-\nu)^2} \right| \leq \sum_{\nu=-\infty}^{+\infty} \frac{1}{(x-\nu)^2 + y^2} \leq 2 \sum_{n=0}^{\infty} \frac{1}{n^2 + y^2};$$

and, since $\sin \pi z = (1/2i)(e^{i\pi z} - e^{-i\pi z})$,

$$\left| \frac{\pi^2}{\sin^2 \pi z} \right| = \frac{4\pi^2}{e^{2\pi y} + e^{-2\pi y} - 2 \cos 2\pi x} < \frac{4\pi^2}{e^{2\pi |y|} - 2}$$

for those z. Consequently,

$$\left| h_0''(z) \right| < 2 \sum_{n=0}^{\infty} \frac{1}{n^2 + y^2} + \frac{4\pi^2}{e^{2\pi |y|} - 2}$$

there, and this expression certainly remains less than a fixed bound for all $| y | \geq 1$. Hence,

$$h_0''(z) = \text{constant} = c''.$$

According to the inequality just obtained, $| h_0''(z) |$ is arbitrarily small if $| y |$ is sufficiently large; hence c'' must be equal to zero. Therefore

$$h_0''(z) = 0, \qquad h_0'(z) = \text{constant} = c',$$

and hence by (2)

$$\pi \cot \pi z = c' + \frac{1}{z} + \sum_{\nu=1}^{\infty} \frac{2z}{z^2 - \nu^2}.$$

If we substitute $-z$ for z in this equality, we see that $c' = -c'$, and hence $c' = 0$. Then $h_0(z)$ and $e^{h_0(z)}$ are also constant. Therefore

$$\sin \pi z = c \cdot z \cdot \prod_{\nu=1}^{\infty} \left(1 - \frac{z^2}{\nu^2}\right).$$

If we divide through by z and allow z to approach zero, we obtain $\pi = c$. Thus,

$$\sin \pi z = \pi z \cdot \prod_{\nu=1}^{\infty} \left(1 - \frac{z^2}{\nu^2}\right),$$

valid for *all* z, is the *product representation of the sine-function* which we set out to find.

2d Example: Weierstrass's σ-function. Let ω and ω' be two non-zero numbers whose ratio is not real (or: which do not lie in a straight line with the origin). Then an entire function is to be constructed having zeros, of order unity, at all points of the form

$$k\omega + k'\omega', \qquad \begin{cases} k = 0, \pm 1, \pm 2, \cdots \\ k' = 0, \pm 1, \pm 2, \cdots, \end{cases}$$

and at no other points.

Draw the straight lines L, L' joining the origin to the points ω, ω', respectively (see Fig. 1). Mark the points $k\omega$ on L and $k'\omega'$ on L', and through each of these points draw a line parallel to L', L, respectively. The points of intersection of these two families of parallel lines are precisely the given points $k\omega + k'\omega'$. They are the "*lattice points of a network of parallelograms*" determined by ω and ω'.

We can enumerate these lattice points in the follow-

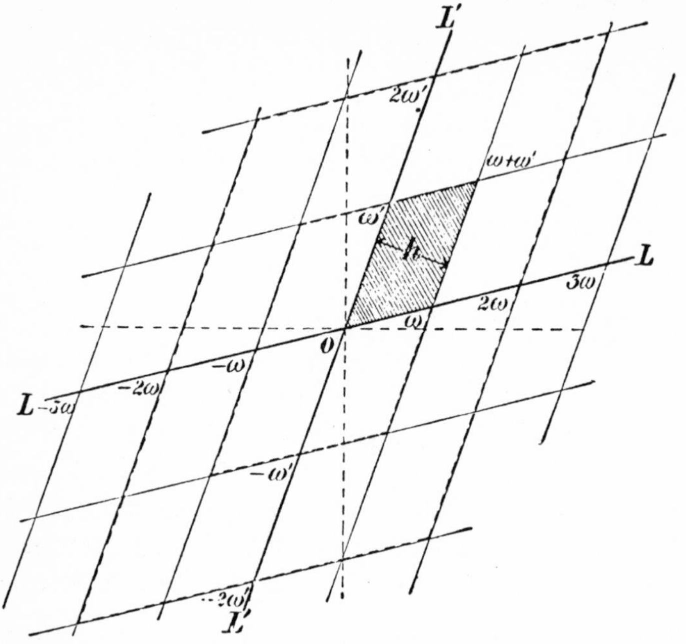

Fig. 1.

ing manner. Consider the parallelograms whose centers lie at the origin, and whose sides are parallel to L, L' and have in turn the lengths 2ω, 4ω, 6ω, 8ω, $\cdots$, $2\omega'$, $4\omega'$, $6\omega'$, $8\omega'$, $\cdots$, respectively. These sides are indicated by interrupted lines in Fig. 1. Now, start with the point O, and number the points lying on the sides of the successive parallelograms; beginning on each parallelogram with the point $k\omega$, and traversing the parallelogram in the mathematically positive sense. We thus obtain a sequence of lattice points, which begins with

$$0, \omega, \omega + \omega', \omega', -\omega + \omega', -\omega, -\omega - \omega', -\omega',$$

$$\omega - \omega', 2\omega, 2\omega + \omega', 2\omega + 2\omega', \cdots .$$

Keeping the points in this order, we denote them by $z_0, z_1, z_2, \cdots$. First we shall show that the series

$$\sum_{\nu=1}^{\infty} \left(\frac{z}{z_\nu}\right)^3$$

is absolutely convergent for every z. Let us number the parallelograms, along which we just counted the lattice points, the 1st, 2d, 3d, $\cdots$ according to size. On the pth one of these lie precisely $8p$ of our lattice points, whose absolute values, moreover, are greater than or equal to ph, if h denotes the smaller of the two altitudes of the "*fundamental parallelogram*" with vertices 0, ω, $\omega + \omega'$, ω'. Hence, the points of the pth parallelogram contribute to the series $\sum \left|\frac{z}{z_\nu}\right|^3$ an absolute value which is less than or equal to

$$8p\left(\frac{|z|}{ph}\right)^3 = \frac{8\,|z|^3}{h^3}\cdot\frac{1}{p^2}.$$

Since $\Sigma(1/p^2)$ converges, the series above also converges absolutely for every z. It is therefore sufficient to take all $k_\nu = 3$ in the Weierstrass product, and

$$G_0(z) = z \cdot \prod_{\nu=1}^{\infty} \cdot \left[\left(1 - \frac{z}{z_\nu}\right) \exp\left\{\frac{z}{z_\nu} + \frac{1}{2}\left(\frac{z}{z_\nu}\right)^2\right\}\right]$$

is, with the meaning given to the z_ν, an entire function with the required properties. In the Weierstrassian theory of elliptic functions, this function is called the **Sigma-function** belonging to the pair of periods (ω, ω'), and is denoted by

$$\sigma(z) = \sigma(z \mid \tfrac{1}{2}\omega, \tfrac{1}{2}\omega').$$

Because of the absolute convergence of the product, the order in which the factors appear does not matter any more (see §2, Theorem 6). Hence, without further establishing the sequence of the lattice points, we can write

$$\sigma(z \mid \tfrac{1}{2}\omega, \tfrac{1}{2}\omega')$$

$$= z \cdot \prod_{k,k'}{}' \left[\left(1 - \frac{z}{k\omega + k'\omega'}\right) \cdot \exp\left\{\frac{z}{k\omega + k'\omega'} + \frac{1}{2}\left(\frac{z}{k\omega + k'\omega'}\right)^2\right\}\right].$$

Here k and k' take on independently of each other all positive and negative integral values and zero, without, however, being zero *simultaneously*. This last restriction is indicated by the accent after the product symbol.

3d Example. Finally, we shall construct an entire function which has zeros, of order unity, at $z_0 = 0$, $z_1 = -1$, $z_2 = -2$, $\cdots$, $z_\nu = -\nu$, $\cdots$, and at no other point. Here it is obviously sufficient again to take all $k_\nu = 2$, so that

$$G(z) = e^{h(z)} \cdot z \cdot \prod_{\nu=1}^{\infty} \left[\left(1 + \frac{z}{\nu}\right) e^{-z/\nu}\right]$$

is the most general function with the required properties. It is closely related to the so-called (**Eulerian**) **Gamma-function,** which, for real values of the argument, is familiar to the reader from the integral calculus, and which was defined by Gauss for arbitrary complex $z \neq 0, -1, -2, \cdots$ by means of the limit

$$\Gamma(z) = \lim_{n \to \infty} \frac{n!\, n^z}{z(z+1)(z+2)\cdots(z+n)}$$

$$(n^z = e^{z \log n}, \text{ with } \log n \text{ real and positive}).^1$$

It is easy to see that this limit exists for all z in question. For if we write the reciprocal of the expression under consideration in the form

$$e^{-z \log n} \cdot z \cdot \left(1 + \frac{z}{1}\right)\left(1 + \frac{z}{2}\right) \cdots \left(1 + \frac{z}{n}\right),$$

[1]After the elementary functions, the Gamma-function is one of the most important functions of analysis. It is met with in the most varied investigations of pure and applied mathematics, from the theory of numbers to theoretical physics, so that an intimate knowledge of its analytical properties is absolutely indispensable.

The first study of this function is to be traced back to the problem of *interpolating* the sequence of factorials $0!(=1), 1!, 2!, \cdots$; i.e., joining the points $(\nu, \nu!)$ or (as one usually writes, following Euler) the points with coordinates $x = \nu + 1$, $y = \nu!$ ($\nu = 0, 1, 2, \cdots$) by as simple a curve as possible. This is the problem of finding the simplest real function $y = F(x)$ of the real variable x, such that $y = \nu!$ for $x = \nu + 1$. Euler gave as a solution the integral $\int_0^\infty e^{-t} t^{z-1}\, dt$, which converges for all $\Re(z) > 0$; Gauss, the limit mentioned in the text. Both solutions yield the *same* function for $\Re(z) > 0$. For lack of space we must suppress the proof of this last assertion. An especially elementary proof has been given by A. Pringsheim, Math. Ann. 31 (1888), pp. 455-481.

it is further equal to

$$\left[\exp\left\{\left(1 + \frac{1}{2} + \cdots + \frac{1}{n} - \log n\right)z\right\}\right] \cdot$$

$$\cdot z \cdot \prod_{\nu=1}^{n} \left[\left(1 + \frac{z}{\nu}\right) e^{-z/\nu}\right].$$

Now, as is well known,

$$\lim_{n \to \infty} \left[\left(1 + \frac{1}{2} + \cdots + \frac{1}{n}\right) - \log n\right] = C$$

exists.[1] Therefore, as $n \to \infty$, our last expression tends

[1]It is immediately evident from the geometrical interpretation of the integral as a plane area, that

$$1/n > \int_n^{n+1} (dx/x) > 1/(n + 1) \text{ and hence}$$

$$(1/n) - (1/(n + 1)) > (1/n) - \int_n^{n+1} (dx/x) > 0$$

for every $n = 1, 2, \cdots$. If we set $(1/n) - \int_n^{n+1} (dx/x) = \gamma_n$, then $0 < \gamma_n < (1/n) - (1/(n+1))$. Therefore $\Sigma\gamma_n = C$ is convergent, with $0 < C < 1$. Consequently

$$(\gamma_1 + \gamma_2 + \cdots + \gamma_{n-1})$$

$$= [1 + (1/2) + \cdots + (1/(n - 1))] - \int_1^n (dx/x) \to C;$$

and, since $1/n \to 0$ and $\int_1^n (dx/x) = \log n$,

$$[(1 + (1/2) + \cdots + (1/n)) - \log n] \to C.$$

C is called Euler's or Mascheroni's constant. Its value lies between zero and one; more precisely: $C = 0.5772156649 \cdots$.

(actually for every z) to the value of the entire function

$$K(z) = e^{Cz} \cdot z \cdot \prod_{\nu=1}^{\infty} \left[\left(1 + \frac{z}{\nu}\right) e^{-z/\nu} \right],$$

which results from the solution of our last example by setting $h(z) = Cz$. Since $K(z)$ is certainly different from zero for $z \neq 0, -1, -2, \cdots$, the Gaussian limit as formulated above exists and is equal to $\frac{1}{K(z)}$. It thus defines a single-valued analytic function, namely, the reciprocal of the entire function $K(z)$. (For further details, see §6, 3d Example).

Exercises. 1. Derive the values of the following three products from the sine-product:

a) $$\frac{2}{1} \cdot \frac{2}{3} \cdot \frac{4}{3} \cdot \frac{4}{5} \cdot \frac{6}{5} \cdot \frac{6}{7} \cdots$$

(Wallis's Product)

b) $$\frac{2}{1} \cdot \frac{2}{3} \cdot \frac{6}{5} \cdot \frac{6}{7} \cdot \frac{10}{9} \cdot \frac{10}{11} \cdot \frac{14}{13} \cdots$$

c) $$2 \cdot \frac{2}{3} \cdot \frac{4}{3} \cdot \frac{8}{9} \cdot \frac{10}{9} \cdot \frac{14}{15} \cdot \frac{16}{15} \cdots .$$

2. Obtain the product expansions of the following entire functions:

a) $e^z - 1$; b) $e^z - e^{z_0}$; c) $\sin z - \sin z_0$; $\cos z - \cos z_0$.

3. Demonstrate the existence of entire functions which assume arbitrarily prescribed values $w_1, w_2, \cdots, w_n, \cdots$ at arbitrarily assigned points $z_1, z_2, \cdots, z_n, \cdots$, respectively, having no finite limit point.

CHAPTER 2

MEROMORPHIC FUNCTIONS

§4. Mittag-Leffler's Partial-fractions-theorem

The fractional rational functions are completely characterized in a purely function-theoretical manner by Theorems 1-3 in I, §35. Analogous to our procedure in the preceding chapter, we express the fundamental properties of these functions in the following two statements:

(A) For every (fractional) rational function there is a so-called *decomposition into partial fractions*, which displays its poles and the corresponding principal parts.

Thus, let $f_0(z)$ be the given rational function, and let $z_1, z_2, \cdots, z_k$ be its poles with the corresponding principal parts

$$(1)\quad h_\nu(z) = \frac{a_{-1}^{(\nu)}}{z - z_\nu} + \frac{a_{-2}^{(\nu)}}{(z - z_\nu)^2} + \cdots + \frac{a_{-\alpha_\nu}^{(\nu)}}{(z - z_\nu)^{\alpha_\nu}},$$

$$(\nu = 1, 2, \cdots, k).$$

Then we can set

$$(2)\quad f_0(z) = g_0(z) + h_1(z) + h_2(z) + \cdots + h_k(z),$$

where $g_0(z)$ is a suitable *entire* rational function. We infer at once from this decomposition into partial fractions, that every other rational function $f(z)$ having the same poles with the same respective principal parts can differ from $f_0(z)$ in the term $g_0(z)$ alone. Furthermore, one can arbitrarily assign these poles and their principal parts. In other words:

(B) It is always possible to construct a rational function whose poles and their principal parts are prescribed. This function can be represented as a partial-fractions decomposition which displays these poles and their principal parts. The most general function of this kind is obtained from a particular one by adding to it an arbitrary *entire* rational function.

These fundamental facts concerning rational functions can again be carried over in all particulars to the more general class of meromorphic functions, whose definition we have already indicated in the Introduction, and which we shall now state more precisely.

Definition. *A single-valued function shall—without regard to its behavior at infinity—be called meromorphic, if it has no singularities other than* (*at most*) *poles in the entire plane.*

On the basis of this definition we have the following theorem:

Theorem 1. *A meromorphic function has in every finite region at most a finite number of poles.*

For otherwise there would exist a finite limit point of poles, and this point would be singular, but certainly not a pole.

According to this, the rational functions are special cases of meromorphic functions, and the entire functions must also be regarded as such.

The function $\dfrac{1}{\sin z}$ is meromorphic; because in the finite part of the plane it has a singularity, namely a pole of order unity, only wherever $\sin z$ has a zero. We see, likewise, that $\cot z = \frac{1}{\sin z} \cdot \cos z$ and $\tan z$ are meromorphic functions. More generally, if $G(z)$ denotes any entire function, its reciprocal, $1/G(z)$, is a meromorphic function (and hence, e.g., the function $\Gamma(z) = 1/K(z)$, considered at the end of the preceding paragraph, is meromorphic). For, $1/G(z)$ has poles (but otherwise no singularities) at those, and only those, points at which $G(z)$ has zeros; and the orders of both are the same. If $G_1(z)$ is an entire function which has no zeros in common with $G(z)$, we see that $G_1(z)/G(z)$ is a meromorphic function whose poles coincide in position and order (although, in general, not in their principal parts) with those of $1/G(z)$.[1]

We now again set ourselves the **problem** which corresponds to the second statement (B). We propose to investigate whether, and how, one can construct a meromorphic function if its poles and the corresponding principal parts are prescribed, and to what extent a meromorphic function is determined by these conditions.

This last question can be answered immediately. If $M_0(z)$ and $M(z)$ are two meromorphic functions which

[1]This last example represents the most general case; for there is the following **Theorem:** *Every meromorphic function $f(z)$ can be expressed as the quotient of two entire functions having no zeros in common.* Proof: The poles of $f(z)$ have no finite limit point. According to Weierstrass's factor-theorem, we can construct an entire function $G(z)$ whose *zeros* coincide in position and order with the *poles* of $f(z)$. Then $f(z) \cdot G(z)$ is evidently an *entire* function, $G_1(z)$. Hence, $f(z) = G_1(z)/G(z)$; and $G_1(z)$ has no zero in common with $G(z)$.

coincide in their poles and the corresponding principal parts, then their difference, $M(z) - M_0(z)$, is evidently an *entire* function. Consequently, they differ by at most an (additive) entire function ("a meromorphic function with no poles"). Conversely, since the addition of such a function to $M_0(z)$ does not alter its poles or the corresponding principal parts, we are able to say the following:

Theorem 2. *Let $M_0(z)$ be a particular meromorphic function. Then, if $G(z)$ denotes an arbitrary entire function,*

$$M(z) = M_0(z) + G(z)$$

is the most general meromorphic function which coincides with $M_0(z)$ in its poles and the corresponding principal parts.

There remains only the investigation of the possibility and method of constructing a particular meromorphic function with arbitrarily prescribed poles.

According to Theorem 1, the set of assigned poles cannot have a finite limit point. If this is excluded, however, then the problem posed can be solved without any further restriction. The following theorem is named after its discoverer:

Mittag-Leffler's partial-fractions-theorem. *Let any finite or infinite set of points having no finite limit point be prescribed, and associate with each of its points a principal part, i.e., a rational function of the special form* (1). *Then there exists a meromorphic function which has poles with the prescribed principal parts at precisely the prescribed points, and is otherwise regular. It can be* *represented in the form of a partial-fractions decomposition (see p.* 40 *for the final form) from which one can read off again the poles along with their principal parts. Further, by Theorem* 2, *if* $M_0(z)$ *is one such function,*

$$M(z) = M_0(z) + G(z)$$

is the most general function satisfying the conditions of the problem, if $G(z)$ *denotes an arbitrary entire function.*

This theorem solves the problem which corresponds to statement (B) concerning rational functions. Let us regard it for the moment as having been proved. Then the solution of the problem corresponding to statement (A) also follows immediately therefrom. For, let $M(z)$ be an arbitrarily given meromorphic function. The set of its poles has no finite limit point. Hence, according to Mittag-Leffler's theorem, another meromorphic function, $M_0(z)$, having the same poles and principal parts as $M(z)$, can be constructed in the form of a partial-fractions decomposition displaying these. Then, by Theorem 2,

$$M(z) = M_0(z) + G_0(z),$$

where $G_0(z)$ denotes a suitable entire function. We have thus actually obtained a decomposition of the *given* meromorphic function $M(z)$ into partial fractions, from which its poles and the corresponding principal parts can be read off.

Exercises. 1. $\cot z$ and $\dfrac{2i}{e^{2iz} - 1}$ are two meromorphic functions which coincide in their poles and the corresponding principal parts. (Proof?) According to Theorem 2, the first differs from the second only by an (additive) entire function. Find this function.

2. The same for the functions

$$\frac{1}{2i \cos z} \text{ and } \frac{\sin z}{e^{2iz} + 1}.$$

§5. Proof of Mittag-Leffler's Theorem

If the function to be constructed is to have no poles at all, then every entire function is a solution of the problem. If it is to have the finitely many poles z_1, $z_2, \cdots, z_k$ with the respective principal parts $h_1(z)$, $h_2(z), \cdots, h_k(z)$, then evidently

$$M_0(z) = h_1(z) + h_2(z) + \cdots + h_k(z)$$

is a solution. If, however, an infinite number of poles are prescribed, we cannot attain our goal so simply; because the analogous series, now infinite, would diverge in general. Nevertheless, we can *produce* the convergence, as in §2, by means of a suitable modification of the terms of the series.

To this end, we make exactly the same agreements regarding the enumeration of the poles as we did in §2, p. 17 in connection with the zeros. If the origin is a prescribed pole, we denote it by z_0 and leave it aside for the time being. Let $h_0(z), h_1(z), \cdots, h_\nu(z), \cdots$ be the principal parts corresponding to the points $z_0, z_1, \cdots,$ $z_\nu, \cdots$; $h_\nu(z)$ is understood to be an expression of the type appearing in formula (1), p. 34. Each of these functions $h_\nu(z)$, $\nu = 1, 2, 3, \cdots$, is regular in a neighborhood of the origin. Its power-series expansion

$$h_\nu(z) = a_0^{(\nu)} + a_1^{(\nu)}z + a_2^{(\nu)}z^2 + \cdots \qquad (\nu = 1, 2, \cdots)$$

for this neighborhood converges for all $|z| < |z_\nu|$; hence, it is *uniformly* convergent for all $|z| \leq \frac{1}{2}|z_\nu|$. Consequently (for every $\nu = 1, 2, 3, \cdots$) an integer n_ν can be determined such that the remainder of the power series after the n_νth term remains, in absolute value, less than any preassigned positive number, e.g., $\frac{1}{2^\nu}$. We denote the sum of the first n_ν terms of the series by $g_\nu(z)$. Thus, $g_\nu(z)$ is an entire rational function of degree n_ν:

$$g_\nu(z) = a_0^{(\nu)} + a_1^{(\nu)}z + \cdots + a_{n_\nu}^{(\nu)}z^{n_\nu} \quad (\nu = 1, 2, 3, \cdots),$$

and for all $|z| \leq \frac{1}{2}|z_\nu|$ we have

$$|h_\nu(z) - g_\nu(z)| < \frac{1}{2^\nu}.$$

Then

$$M_0(z) = h_0(z) + \sum_{\nu=1}^{\infty} [h_\nu(z) - g_\nu(z)]$$

(Mittag-Leffler's partial-fractions-theorem)

is a meromorphic function satisfying the conditions of the theorem. (If the origin is not assigned as a pole, the term $h_0(z)$ must, of course, be omitted.)

To prove this, we must merely show that the right-hand side defines an analytic function having in every finite domain, e.g., a circle with radius R about the origin as center, exactly the prescribed singularities and no others.

Now, $| z_\nu | \rightarrow +\infty$. Therefore it is possible to choose m so large, that $| z_\nu | > 2R$, and hence $R < \frac{1}{2} | z_\nu |$, for all $\nu > m$. Then, for all $| z | \leq R$ and all $\nu > m$,

$$| z | < \tfrac{1}{2} | z_\nu | \text{ and consequently } | h_\nu(z) - g_\nu(z) | < \frac{1}{2^\nu}.$$

Hence, for all $| z | \leq R$, the series

$$\sum_{\nu=m+1}^{\infty} [h_\nu(z) - g_\nu(z)]$$

is (absolutely and) *uniformly* convergent. Since its terms are regular for $| z | \leq R$ (because the poles of the $h_\nu(z)$ with $\nu > m$ lie *outside* the circle $| z | = R$), it defines there a regular function which we shall denote by $F_m(z)$. Then evidently

$$M_0(z) = h_0(z) + \sum_{\nu=1}^{m} [h_\nu(z) - g_\nu(z)] + F_m(z)$$

is also an analytic function which is regular in the circle with radius R about the origin as center, with the exception of those points z_ν in this circle which are poles with principal parts $h_\nu(z)$. The same is valid for every finite region, because R was completely arbitrary; and hence, $M_0(z)$ is a meromorphic function with the required properties.

From the proof it follows that it is sufficient to take the degree n_ν of the polynomial $g_\nu(z)$ (the sum of the first n_ν terms of the power series for $h_\nu(z)$) so large, that, having chosen an arbitrary $R > 0$, the terms $| h_\nu(z) - g_\nu(z) |$ for all $| z | \leq R$ finally (i.e., for all sufficiently large ν) remain less than the terms of a convergent series of positive terms.

Exercises. 1. Does the Mittag-Leffler theorem still hold if the prescribed principal parts contain an infinite number of negative powers? How do the theorem and its proof read then?

2. In connection with Mittag-Leffler's theorem, can one assign the *ascending* part of the Laurent expansion —or at least a finite number of its terms—at all points z_ν (or at several, or one)?

3. The Mittag-Leffler theorem, like the Weierstrass theorem (see §2, Ex. 7), can be carried over to the unit circle. Formulate and prove the theorem indicated.

4. Solve Exercise 3, §3 once again, with the means that have now been developed.

§6. Examples of Mittag-Leffler's Theorem

At times, the "convergence-producing terms" $g_\nu(z)$ are not at all necessary; cf. the analogous case in connection with Weierstrass's theorem. Then, of course, the function to be constructed is especially simple. If, e.g., the points $0, 1, 4, \cdots, \nu^2, \cdots$ are to be poles of order unity with respective principal parts $\dfrac{1}{z - \nu^2}$, then

$$M_0(z) = \frac{1}{z} + \sum_{\nu=1}^{\infty} \frac{1}{z - \nu^2} = \sum_{\nu=0}^{\infty} \frac{1}{z - \nu^2}$$

is a solution. For, let $R > 0$ be chosen arbitrarily, and $m > \sqrt{2R}$. Then the series from $\nu = m + 1$ on is evidently uniformly convergent in $|z| \leq R$,[1] which proves our assertion.

We proceed to construct meromorphic functions corresponding to the examples in §3.

1st Example: cot πz. The real lattice points are to be poles of order unity with the residue $+1$, and hence, with the principal parts

$$h_\nu(z) = \frac{1}{z - z_\nu}, \qquad (z_0 = 0,\ z_{2\nu-1} = \nu,\ z_{2\nu} = -\nu).$$

For $\nu = 1, 2, 3, \cdots$,

$$h_\nu(z) = -\frac{1}{z_\nu} - \frac{z}{z_\nu^2} - \frac{z^2}{z_\nu^3} - \cdots,$$

and it suffices to take all $n_\nu = 0$, and hence,

$$g_\nu(z) = -\frac{1}{z_\nu};$$

because then for all sufficiently large ν (namely, for all $\nu > 4R$) and all $|z| \leq R$,

$$|h_\nu(z) - g_\nu(z)| \leq \frac{R}{|z_\nu|(|z_\nu| - R)} < \frac{2R}{|z_\nu|^2},$$

so that the $|h_\nu(z) - g_\nu(z)|$ finally remain less than the terms of an obviously convergent series of positive terms. Consequently, according to the concluding remark of the preceding paragraph, if $G(z)$ is an arbitrary entire function,

[1]Because for $\nu > m$ and $|z| \leq R$ we have

$$|1/(z - \nu^2)| \leq 1/(\nu^2 - R) < 1/(\nu^2 - \tfrac{1}{2}\nu^2) = 2/\nu^2.$$

$$M(z) = G(z) + \frac{1}{z} + \sum_{\nu=1}^{\infty} \left[\frac{1}{z - z_\nu} + \frac{1}{z_\nu}\right]$$

$$= G(z) + \frac{1}{z} + \sum_{\nu=1}^{\infty} \left(\left[\frac{1}{z - \nu} + \frac{1}{\nu}\right] + \left[\frac{1}{z + \nu} - \frac{1}{\nu}\right]\right)$$

$$= G(z) + \frac{1}{z} + \sum_{\nu=1}^{\infty} \left[\frac{1}{z - \nu} + \frac{1}{z + \nu}\right]$$

is the most general function of the kind required.

The function $\cot \pi z$ also has poles of order unity at the points $0, \pm 1, \pm 2, \cdots$ (cf. I, p. 126, 3). If n is one of them, the residue at this point is

$$\lim_{z \to n} \frac{(z - n) \cos \pi z}{\sin \pi z} = \lim_{z \to n} \frac{(z - n)[(-1)^n + \cdots]}{(-1)^n \pi (z - n) + \cdots} = \frac{1}{\pi},$$

which can be read off immediately from the indicated series-expansion for a neighborhood of the point $z = n$. Hence, the function $\pi \cot \pi z$ is contained among the functions $M(z)$ which we just constructed.

We have thus arrived at formula (2) of §3 from an entirely different direction. The still undetermined entire function $G(z)$, which there was called $h_0'(z)$, cannot be ascertained solely from the nature and position of the poles. We should, as before, have to make use of special properties of the function in question. However, in determining the product for $\sin \pi z$, we have already discovered that we have to set $h_0'(z)$, that is, $G(z)$, equal to zero. Therefore

$$\pi \cot \pi z = \frac{1}{z} + \sum_{\nu=1}^{\infty} \left[\frac{1}{z - \nu} + \frac{1}{z + \nu}\right]$$

is the *partial-fractions decomposition of the cotangent-function.*

2d Example: Weierstrass's $\wp$-function. We shall construct a meromorphic function which has a pole of order *two* with the principal part

$$h_\nu(z) = \frac{1}{(z - z_\nu)^2}$$

at each of the lattice points $z_\nu = k\omega + k'\omega'$, $(\nu = 1, 2, 3, \cdots)$, described and enumerated in §3, Example 2. For $\nu = 1, 2, 3, \cdots$,

$$h_\nu(z) = \frac{1}{z_\nu^2} \cdot \frac{1}{(1 - (z/z_\nu))^2} = \frac{1}{z_\nu^2} + 2\frac{z}{z_\nu^3} + 3\frac{z^2}{z_\nu^4} + \cdots,$$

and it is again sufficient to take all $n_\nu = 0$, and hence, to take as $g_\nu(z)$ the first term of this expansion. For then we have

$$h_\nu(z) - g_\nu(z) = \frac{1}{(z - z_\nu)^2} - \frac{1}{z_\nu^2} = \frac{2zz_\nu - z^2}{z_\nu^2(z - z_\nu)^2};$$

and consequently, for all $|z| \leq R$, with arbitrary $R > 0$, and all sufficiently large ν (namely, as soon as $|z_\nu| > 2R$),

$$|h_\nu(z) - g_\nu(z)|$$
$$\leq \frac{R(2|z_\nu| + R)}{|z_\nu|^2(|z_\nu| - R)^2} < \frac{3R|z_\nu|}{|z_\nu|^2(\frac{1}{2}|z_\nu|)^2} = \frac{12R}{|z_\nu|^3}$$

This is (according to §3, p. 29) the general term of a convergent series of positive terms. Hence,

$$M_0(z) = \frac{1}{z^2} + \sum_{\nu=1}^{\infty} \left[\frac{1}{(z - z_\nu)^2} - \frac{1}{z_\nu^2}\right]$$

is a meromorphic function of the type required, and the most general function of this type results immediately therefrom.

In the Weierstrassian theory of elliptic functions, this function $M_0(z)$ is called the **Pe-function** belonging to the pair of periods (ω, ω'), and is denoted by

$$\wp(z) = \wp(z \mid \tfrac{1}{2}\omega, \tfrac{1}{2}\omega').$$

Because of the absolute convergence of the series, the order in which the terms appear does not matter. Hence (cf. p. 30), without further establishing the sequence of the lattice points, we can write

$$\wp(z \mid \tfrac{1}{2}\omega, \tfrac{1}{2}\omega')$$

$$= \frac{1}{z^2} + \sum_{k,k'}{}' \left[\frac{1}{(z - k\omega - k'\omega')^2} - \frac{1}{(k\omega + k'\omega')^2}\right].$$

Here k and k' take on, independently of each other, all positive and negative integral values and zero, without, however, being zero *simultaneously*. This last restriction is indicated by the accent after the summation symbol.

This function $\wp(z)$ bears a close relation to the σ-function of §3, similar to that of cotangent to sine. In fact, according to §2, Theorem 8,

$$\frac{\sigma'}{\sigma}(z) = \frac{1}{z} + \sum_{\nu=1}^{\infty} \left[\frac{1}{z - z_\nu} + \frac{1}{z_\nu} + \frac{z}{z_\nu^2}\right],[1]$$

[1] $\frac{\sigma'}{\sigma}(z)$ is an abbreviated notation for $\frac{\sigma'(z)}{\sigma(z)}$. This function is frequently called the Weierstrass ζ-function, and denoted by $\zeta(z)$. It has, of course, nothing to do with the Riemann ζ-function

and further, by §2, Theorem 9,

$$-\frac{d}{dz}\left(\frac{\sigma'}{\sigma}(z)\right) = \frac{1}{z^2} + \sum_{\nu=1}^{\infty}\left[\frac{1}{(z - z_\nu)^2} - \frac{1}{z_\nu^2}\right] = \wp(z).$$

Hence,

$$\wp(z) = -\frac{d^2}{dz^2}(\log \sigma(z)) = \frac{(\sigma'(z))^2 - \sigma(z)\,\sigma''(z)}{\sigma^2(z)}.$$

The close connection between Examples 1 and 2 of this paragraph and of §3 suggests the possibility of the existence of a direct relationship between the fundamental theorems themselves—the Weierstrass and the Mittag-Leffler. This is indeed the case: one can derive the first from the second (but not conversely). The method is briefly the following:

Let it be required to construct an entire function $G_0(z)$ with zeros z_ν of respective orders α_ν. First, according to Mittag-Leffler's theorem, construct a meromorphic function $M_0(z)$ having *simple* poles with residues α_ν, and, hence, with principal parts $h_\nu(z) = \dfrac{\alpha_\nu}{z - z_\nu}$, at the points z_ν. One finds, then, almost immediately, that $M_0(z)$ is the logarithmic derivative of an entire function, $G_0(z)$, which can be written in the form of an infinite product, and which satisfies the conditions of Weierstrass's theorem.

---

which is treated in Example 4. At the same time, $\dfrac{\sigma'}{\sigma}(z)$, furnishes us with an example of a meromorphic function which has a simple pole with the residue $+1$ at each of the lattice points of our network of parallelograms.

3d Example: The Gamma-function. The function $\Gamma(z)$, mentioned already in connection with Example 3 of Weierstrass's theorem, proved to be the reciprocal of the entire function $K(z)$ which was constructed there. From this we see immediately that

(1) $\Gamma(z)$ **is a meromorphic function** having a simple pole (for the residue see **(7)** below) only at each of the points $0, -1, -2, \cdots$. Moreover, it is the reciprocal of an entire function, and therefore has no zeros.

We develop several further properties of this important function:

(2) For every $z \neq 0, -1, -2, \cdots$,

$$\Gamma(z + 1) = z\Gamma(z):$$

(Functional equation of the Gamma-function)

Proof:

$$\Gamma(z + 1) = \lim_{n\to\infty} \frac{n!n^{z+1}}{(z + 1)(z + 2) \cdots (z + n + 1)}$$

$$= z \cdot \lim_{n\to\infty} \frac{n!n^z}{z(z + 1) \cdots (z + n)} \cdot \frac{n}{z + n + 1}$$

$$= z\Gamma(z),$$ Q. E. D.

(3) For every integer $\nu \geq 0$,

$$\Gamma(\nu + 1) = \nu!;$$

i.e., $\Gamma(z)$ solves the interpolation problem mentioned on p. 31, footnote.

Proof: For $\nu > 0$, according to **(2)**,

$$\Gamma(\nu + 1) = \nu\Gamma(\nu) = \nu(\nu - 1)\Gamma(\nu - 1) = \cdots = \nu!\Gamma(1);$$

and that $\Gamma(1) = 1$ is seen immediately from the Gaussian definition.

(4) For every z we have[1]

$$\lim_{n\to\infty} \frac{\Gamma(z+n+1)}{n!n^z} = 1.$$

Proof: The Gaussian definition says that, as $n \to \infty$,

$$\frac{n!n^z}{(z+n)(z+n-1)\cdots(z+1)\,z\cdot\Gamma(z)} \to 1.$$

The denominator here is equal to $\Gamma(z+n+1)$, as one finds by applying the functional equation $n+1$ times; and this proves the assertion.

(5) For every non-integral z,

$$\Gamma(z)\Gamma(1-z) = \frac{\pi}{\sin \pi z}.$$

Proof: According to the Gaussian definition, the reciprocal of the left-hand side is equal to

$$\lim_{n\to\infty} \frac{z(z+1)\cdots(z+n)}{n!n^z}\cdot \frac{(1-z)(2-z)\cdots(n+1-z)}{n!n^{1-z}}$$

$$= \lim_{n\to\infty} \frac{n+1-z}{n}\cdot z(1-z^2)\left(1-\frac{z^2}{2^2}\right)\cdots\left(1-\frac{z^2}{n^2}\right)$$

$$= z\cdot\prod_{\nu=1}^{\infty}\left(1-\frac{z^2}{\nu^2}\right) = \frac{\sin \pi z}{\pi}, \qquad \text{Q. E. D.}$$

[1]The functional equation (2) together with this limit relation (4) are *characteristic* for the Γ-function, i.e., there is no analytic function besides $\Gamma(z)$ which satisfies (2) and (4). We must leave the proof of this proposition to the reader.

(6) $$\Gamma(\tfrac{1}{2}) = +\sqrt{\pi}.$$[1]

Proof: For $z = 1/2$, **(5)** yields $[\Gamma(1/2)]^2 = \pi$, from which the assertion follows immediately (because from the Gaussian definition $\Gamma(1/2)$ is read off as positive).

(7) The respective residues at the poles $-\nu$, $(\nu = 0, 1, 2, \cdots)$, established in **(1)**, are

$$a_{-1}^{(\nu)} = \frac{(-1)^\nu}{\nu!}.$$

[1]This singular result can also be written as follows:

$$\frac{n!\sqrt{n}}{\frac{1}{2}(\frac{1}{2}+1)\cdots(\frac{1}{2}+n)} \to \sqrt{\pi};$$

or, after a very simple transformation:

$$\frac{1\cdot 3\cdot 5\cdots(2n-1)}{2\cdot 4\cdot 6\cdots(2n)} \sim \frac{1}{\sqrt{\pi n}}.$$

The symbol "$\sim$" indicates that the limit of the quotient of both sides as $n \to \infty$ is unity; in other words, that both sides are "asymptotically equivalent", as it is customary to say. The left-hand side is none other than the coefficient of z^n in the binomial series

$$\frac{1}{\sqrt{1-z}} = 1 + \tfrac{1}{2}z + \frac{1\cdot 3}{2\cdot 4}z^2 + \cdots + (-1)^n\binom{-\frac{1}{2}}{n}z^n + \cdots;$$

consequently, (6) is synonymous with the statement that

$$(-1)^n\binom{-\frac{1}{2}}{n} \sim \frac{1}{\sqrt{\pi n}}.$$

Finally, instead of (6) we can write:

$$\frac{\pi}{2} = \frac{2}{1}\cdot\frac{2}{3}\cdot\frac{4}{3}\cdot\frac{4}{5}\cdots\frac{2k}{2k-1}\cdot\frac{2k}{2k+1}\cdots,$$

in which form our result proves to be identical with Wallis's product, which is also obtained at once from the sine-product for $z = 1/2$. (Cf. §3, Ex. 1a).)

Proof: According to its meaning, the residue of a simple pole at $z = -\nu$ is obtained by evaluating

$$\lim_{z \to -\nu} (z + \nu)\Gamma(z).$$

By **(2)**, however,

$$\Gamma(z) = \frac{\Gamma(z+1)}{z} = \cdots = \frac{\Gamma(z+\nu+1)}{z(z+1)\cdots(z+\nu)},$$

so that as $z \to -\nu$,

$$(z+\nu)\Gamma(z) \to \frac{\Gamma(1)}{(-\nu)(-\nu+1)\cdots(-2)(-1)} = \frac{(-1)^\nu}{\nu!},$$

Q. E. D.

4th Example: The Riemann ζ-function. The Zeta-function, whose most important function-theoretical properties were established by Riemann, plays a fundamental role in the analytic theory of numbers.

In all that follows, t^z, for positive t, is understood to be the (single-valued) entire function $e^{z \log t}$, where $\log t$ has its real value. Then the terms of the series (cf. I, §17, Ex. 2α)

$$\sum_{n=1}^{\infty} \frac{1}{n^z}$$

are *entire* functions. For the absolute values of these terms in the closed half-plane $\Re(z) \geq 1 + \delta$ ($\delta > 0$ arbitrary) we have

$$\left| \frac{1}{n^z} \right| = \frac{1}{n^{\Re(z)}} \leq \frac{1}{n^{1+\delta}}.$$

Therefore, by Weierstrass's M-test, the series is uniformly convergent there. According to I, §19, Theorem 3, since $\delta > 0$ was arbitrary, this means that the series represents a regular function in the half-plane $\Re(z) > 1$. It is this function which is called the *Riemann Zeta-function* and denoted by $\zeta(z)$.

Theorem. *$\zeta(z)$ can be continued across the boundary $\Re(z) = 1$ of the half-plane $\Re(z) > 1$, and proves to be a meromorphic function having the single pole $z = 1$ with the principal part $1/(z - 1)$; i.e., $z = 1$ is a simple pole with the residue $+1$.*[1]

1st Step: Continuation up to the line $\Re(z) = 0$.

With n^{-z}, the functions $\dfrac{1}{n^{z-1}} - \dfrac{1}{(n+1)^{z-1}}$ for $n =$ 1, 2, $\cdots$ are also entire functions. Since each of these has a zero at $z = 1$,

$$\frac{1}{z-1}\left[\frac{1}{n^{z-1}} - \frac{1}{(n+1)^{z-1}}\right] = \int_0^1 \frac{dt}{(n+t)^z} = \int_n^{n+1} \frac{dt}{t^z}$$

are also *entire* functions. For $\Re(z) \geq 1 + \delta$, the absolute value of the last integral (by I, §11, 5) is less than or equal to $n^{-1-\delta}$. Hence, for the same reason as before,

$$\sum_{n=1}^{\infty} \int_0^1 \frac{dt}{(n+t)^z} = \int_1^{\infty} \frac{dt}{t^z} = \frac{1}{z-1}$$

[1]Stated somewhat differently: the difference $\zeta(z) - (z-1)^{-1}$ is an *entire* (transcendental) *function*.

is convergent for $\Re(z) > 1$. If we subtract this from

$$\sum_{n=1}^{\infty} \frac{1}{(n+1)^z} = \zeta(z) - 1$$

and note that

$$\frac{1}{(n+1)^z} - \int_0^1 \frac{dt}{(n+t)^z} = -z \int_0^1 \frac{t\,dt}{(n+t)^{z+1}}$$

—which can be verified at once by means of an integration by parts on the right-hand side,—we have

$$\text{(a)} \qquad \zeta(z) = 1 + \frac{1}{z-1} - z \sum_{n=1}^{\infty} \int_0^1 \frac{t\,dt}{(n+t)^{z+1}}.$$

Herewith the continuation in question is accomplished. In order to realize this, one need only show, bearing in mind the form of the first two terms on the right, that the third term, or even only that the new series on the right-hand side, represents a regular function for $\Re(z) > 0$. This follows, however, from considerations quite similar to those encountered before: the terms of the series are again *entire* functions (indeed, they arose from the subtraction of such functions!) and in absolute value are less than or equal to $n^{-1-\delta}$ for $\Re(z) \geq \delta$, from which everything follows as above. Consequently, by means of (a), the asserted character of the point $+1$ is made evident; and, moreover, the region of existence of $\zeta(z)$ is extended to the left by a strip of unit width.

In a similar manner, one can repeatedly extend the region of existence to the left by such a strip, and so finally prove the theorem completely. We shall carry out the next two steps.

2d Step: Continuation up to the line $\Re(z) = -1$. Integrating by parts again, one verifies immediately that

$$-z\int_0^1 \frac{t\,dt}{(n+t)^{z+1}}$$

$$= -\frac{z}{2(n+1)^{z+1}} - \frac{z(z+1)}{2}\int_0^1 \frac{t^2\,dt}{(n+t)^{z+2}},$$

and hence

$$\text{(b)} \qquad \zeta(z) = 1 + \frac{1}{z-1} - \frac{z}{2}\,[\zeta(z+1) - 1]$$

$$- \frac{z(z+1)}{2}\sum_{n=1}^{\infty}\int_0^1 \frac{t^2\,dt}{(n+t)^{z+2}}.$$

According to the result of the first step, the function inside the brackets of the third term is regular for $\Re(z) > -1$, except at $z = 0$ where there is a simple pole. Because of the factor z before the bracket, the third term itself is a regular function for $\Re(z) > -1$, with no exceptions. This also holds for the last term, because the terms of the new series are entire functions which, in absolute value, are less than or equal to $n^{-1-\delta}$ for $\Re(z) > -1 + \delta$,—from which everything follows once more.

3d Step: Continuation up to the line $\Re(z) = -2$. Another integration by parts gives

$$\int_0^1 \frac{t^2\,dt}{(n+t)^{z+2}} = \frac{1}{3(n+1)^{z+2}} + \frac{z+2}{3}\int_0^1 \frac{t^3\,dt}{(n+t)^{z+3}},$$

and hence

$$\text{(c)} \qquad \zeta(z) = 1 + \frac{1}{z-1} - \frac{z}{2!}[\zeta(z+1) - 1] - \frac{z(z+1)}{3!}[\zeta(z+2) - 1] - \frac{z(z+1)(z+2)}{3!} \sum_{n=1}^{\infty} \int_0^1 \frac{t^3\,dt}{(n+t)^{z+3}}.$$

Considerations closely corresponding to those just dealt with show that the only singularity of $\zeta(z)$ in the half-plane $\Re(z) > -2$ is the simple pole at $+1$ with the principal part $\frac{1}{z-1}$.

It is now sufficiently clear how one proves that $\zeta(z) - \frac{1}{z-1}$ is regular in the half-plane $\Re(z) > -(k+1)$ if it has already been shown that it is regular in the half-plane $\Re(z) > -k$, $(k = 2, 3, \cdots)$. The truth of all our assertions concerning $\zeta(z)$ is thereby established.[1]

[1]That $\zeta(z) - (z-1)^{-1}$ is a *transcendental* entire function follows, e.g., thus: From the series for $\zeta(z)$, we see immediately that $\lim_{x \to +\infty} \zeta(x) = 1$. If the difference in question were a *rational* entire function, it would be *identically* equal to one, so that $\zeta(z) = 1 + (z-1)^{-1}$. That this is false, however, is seen for $z = 2$.

A full treatment of the Riemann ζ-function, including all number-theoretical applications, is to be found in E. Landau, *Handbuch der Lehre von der Verteilung der Primzahlen*, 2 vols., Leipzig, 1909, and E. Landau, *Vorlesungen über Zahlentheorie*, 3 vols., Leipzig, 1927. See also A. E. Ingham, *The Distribution of Prime Numbers*, Cambridge Tracts, No. 30, 1932; E. C. Titchmarsh, *The Zeta-function of Riemann*, Cambridge Tracts, No. 26, 1930.

Exercises. 1. Find the Mittag-Leffler partial-fractions-expansion for each of the following meromorphic functions:

a) $\tan z$; b) $\dfrac{1}{\sin z}$; c) $\dfrac{\pi}{\cos (\pi/2)z}$

d) $\dfrac{1}{e^z - 1}$ e) $\dfrac{1}{e^z + 1}$; f) $\dfrac{1}{\cos z - \sin z}$.

2. The sequence of functions

$$f_n(z) = \frac{n!n^z}{z(z+1)\cdots(z+n)}$$

is *uniformly* convergent in every bounded, closed region containing none of the points $0, -1, -2, \cdots$.

3. Let z_1 and z_2 be two points distinct from $0, -1, -2, \cdots$. Determine

$$\lim_{n\to\infty} \frac{z_1(z_1+1)\cdots(z_1+n)}{z_2(z_2+1)\cdots(z_2+n)}.$$

4. The entire function $K(z)$ defined in the text has the following representation as an integral:

$$K(z) = \frac{1}{\Gamma(z)} = \frac{1}{2\pi i}\int_k e^t t^{-z}\,dt,$$

where k denotes a path which begins on the left at infinity, proceeds close *below* the negative real axis to a neighborhood of the origin, turns about this point in the positive direction, and then returns to infinity close *above* the negative real axis. (Pay attention to the multiple-valuedness of t^{-z}—as a function of t, for fixed z; details concerning this in sec. II.)

5. Carry out in detail the derivation, sketched in the text, of Weierstrass's theorem from Mittag-Leffler's.

6. Prove the fact mentioned on p. 49, footnote, that the Γ-function is characterized uniquely by the two properties **2** and **4** (pp. 48-9).

7. In connection with §2, Ex.4a, show that the Riemann ζ-function has no zeros in the half-plane $\Re(z) > 1$.

CHAPTER 3

PERIODIC FUNCTIONS

§7. The Periods of Analytic Functions

Definition. *An analytic function $f(z)$ is said to be periodic if there exists a non-zero number Ω such that for every z of the domain of regularity of $f(z)$, $z + \Omega$ also belongs to this domain, and*

$$(1) \qquad f(z + \Omega) = f(z).$$

Every such number Ω is called a period of $f(z)$.

Among the elementary functions, e^z and the trigonometric functions are periodic. $\tan z$ has, e.g., the period -7π; 13π and 2π are also periods of $\tan z$.

In order to confine our attention to what is most important, we shall assume in the following that $f(z)$, except for possible isolated singularities, is single-valued and regular in the entire plane (so that, in particular, entire and meromorphic functions come under consideration). On the other hand, $f(z)$ is not to reduce to a constant, since otherwise equation (1) would be trivial.

If in (1) we replace z by $z + \Omega$, we see that, along with Ω, 2Ω is also a period of the function. The following more general theorem is just as easy to prove:

Theorem 1. *The sum and difference of two periods of a function are also periods of the same;*[1] *if $n, n' \gtreqless 0$ denote*

[1]If $f(z)$ is periodic, the number 0 is also classed with its periods; this is to be noted here and in the following.

any integers, then, along with Ω, all numbers $n\Omega$ are periods, and, along with Ω and Ω', all numbers $n\Omega + n'\Omega'$ are periods.

We now suppose the points corresponding to all the periods of a function, the so-called "period-points", to be marked in the plane. Then we have the important

Theorem 2. *The set of period-points of a single-valued function has no finite limit point.*

Proof: Otherwise every neighborhood of this limit point would contain an infinite number of period-points, and hence, also such period-points having an arbitrarily small distance (= absolute value of the difference) from each other. Then, according to Theorem 1, there would exist periods with arbitrarily small absolute values, and one could determine a sequence of periods $\Omega_1, \Omega_2, \cdots$ such that $\Omega_n \to 0$. If, now, z_0 is an arbitrary regular point of $f(z)$, and $f(z_0) = a$, then for every $n = 1, 2, 3, \cdots$ we should have

$$f(z_0 + \Omega_n) = f(z_0) = a,$$

implying the existence of a-points in every neighborhood of z_0. But this is impossible, according to I, §21, Theorem 1, since we have assumed that $f(z)$ is not constant. The theorem thus proved can be formulated as follows:

Theorem 3. *A single-valued function cannot have arbitrarily small periods.*

From these theorems, which provide us with a first orientation, we can immediately derive some important consequences.

Let $f(z)$ have the period Ω. The numbers $n\Omega$, which, according to Theorem 1, are also periods, all lie on the line L passing through 0 and Ω, and there constitute a set of equidistant points (see Fig. 2). Suppose there exists a further period-point on L (e.g., tan z with the period -7π has, in addition to the periods $-7\pi n$, the period 3π). It must be of the form

$$n\Omega + \theta\Omega, \qquad (n \text{ integral}, 0 < \theta < 1).$$

Then, by Theorem 1, $\theta\Omega$ itself is a period. Thus, if there exist any periods at all on L besides the periods $n\Omega$, then there are some between 0 and Ω. But there can be only a finite number of these (because of Theorem 2), so that one of them lies nearest to 0. We shall call this one ω,[1] and we now have

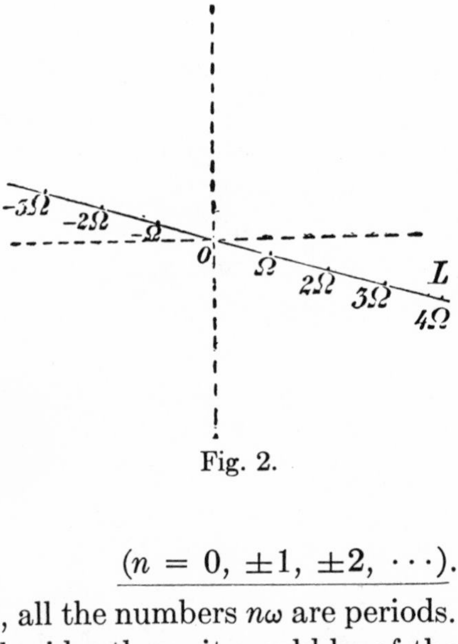

Fig. 2.

Theorem 4. *Every period on L is of the form*

$$n\omega, \qquad (n = 0, \pm 1, \pm 2, \cdots).$$

Proof: By Theorem 1, all the numbers $n\omega$ are periods. If there were one on L besides these, it would be of the form $n\omega + \theta\omega$, $(0 < \theta < 1)$. But then $\theta\omega$, i.e., a point on L between 0 and ω, would also be a period, contrary to the assumption that ω is the period-point on L nearest to 0.

[1]If no further period lies between 0 and Ω, we set $\omega = \Omega$.

By this procedure, ω on L is fully determined except for (the unessential) sign, and is called a **primitive period** of $f(z)$.

The function tan z has, e.g., the period $\Omega = -7\pi$; L here is the axis of reals. There are six additional periods of tan z between 0 and -7π, namely, $-\pi$, -2π, $\cdots$, -6π, of which $-\pi$ is the one nearest to 0. Hence, $-\pi$ is a *primitive period* of tan z, so that *all* periods lying on L (i.e. in this case, all *real* periods) have the form $-n\pi$.

If the function has no periods besides the periods $n\omega$ found in this manner, the function is said to be **simply periodic.** In the other case, the periods do not all lie on one straight line, but form, rather, a *plane* point set. We acquire an insight into the nature of this set in the following manner.

Since, according to Theorem 2, there are only a finite number of period-points in any circle, there must exist a *smallest* circle, with center 0, on which there are one or more periods (distinct from 0) (see Fig. 3). We call one of these ω; it is necessarily a primitive period of the function, and on the line L through 0 and ω there are precisely the periods $n\omega$ and no others. We suppose them to be erased for the moment. Then again there exists a smallest circle, with center 0, on which there are one or more of the remaining periods. Let us call that one of them (there are certainly only a finite number) ω' which we first meet in describing this circle in the positive direction if we begin at that half of the line L which extends from 0 to ω. Then the following theorem completely settles the question as to the distribution of the period-points:

Theorem 5. *All period-points of the function are given by*

$$n\omega + n'\omega', \qquad \begin{cases} n = 0, \pm 1, \pm 2, \cdots \\ n' = 0, \pm 1, \pm 2, \cdots \end{cases}$$

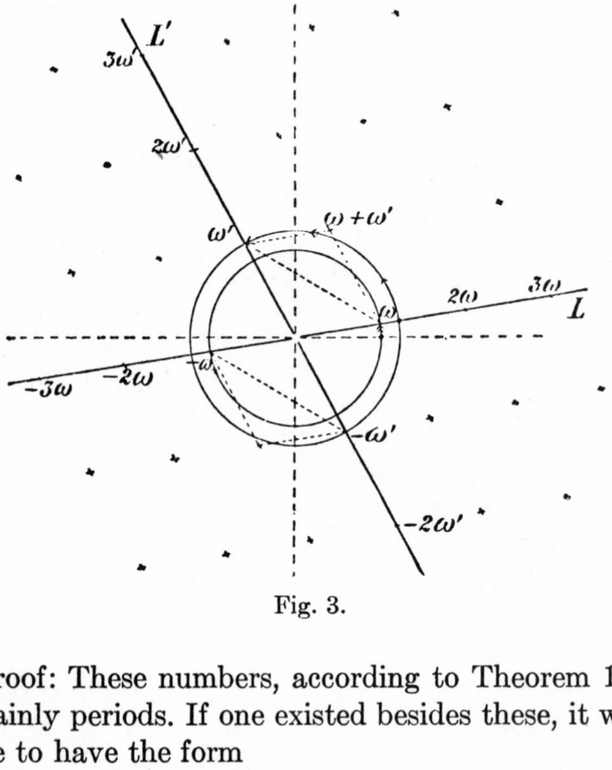

Fig. 3.

Proof: These numbers, according to Theorem 1, are certainly periods. If one existed besides these, it would have to have the form

$$(n + \theta)\omega + (n' + \theta')\omega', \quad 0 \leq \theta \leq 1, 0 \leq \theta' \leq 1,$$

with θ and θ' *not simultaneously* integral (i.e., 0 or 1). But then

$$\Omega = \theta\omega + \theta'\omega'$$

would also be a period. This point would lie in the

parallelogram with the vertices $0, \omega, \omega + \omega', \omega'$, without coinciding with any of the vertices. According to the method used to determine ω and ω', it certainly could not lie in the triangle $0, \omega, \omega'$, and would therefore have to lie in the other half of the parallelogram in question. But, with Ω,

$$\Omega' = -\Omega + \omega + \omega'$$

would also be a period; and it would be in the triangle $0, \omega, \omega'$, where, however, as just shown, there can be no period. Hence, the assumption that there exist periods other than the points $n\omega + n'\omega'$ is inadmissible.

Thus, if a single-valued periodic function is not simply periodic, its periods have the position described by Theorem 5. It will be shown presently (p. 78) that such functions exist. A function of this kind is called **doubly periodic,** and we have

Theorem 6. *The periodicity of a single-valued analytic function can be only simple or double; there is no third.*[1]

The numbers ω and ω' are called a **pair of primitive periods** of the function. Since they are not collinear with 0, their ratio is necessarily non-real:[2]

$$\Re\left(\frac{\omega'}{i\omega}\right) \gtrless 0.$$

[1]We call k complex numbers $\omega_1, \omega_2, \cdots, \omega_k$ *linearly independent,* if no system of k real, integral numbers $n_1, n_2, \cdots, n_k$, not all zero, exists, such that $n_1\omega_1 + n_2\omega_2 + \cdots + n_k\omega_k = 0$. Then this theorem can be stated as follows: "*A single-valued analytic function cannot possess more than two linearly independent periods.*"

[2]The imaginary part of the "period-ratio" ω'/ω is actually *positive* for our determination of the pair of primitive periods, because the positive rotation which carries the direction $(0 \cdots \omega)$ into the direction $(0 \cdots \omega')$ is less than π.

Whereas in the case of a simply periodic function a primitive period, apart from the (quite unessential) sign, is uniquely determined, one can determine a pair of primitive periods of a doubly periodic function in various (infinitely many) ways (cf. Figs. 1 and 3, where the *same* set of points of the form $n\omega + n'\omega'$ is obtained with *different* meanings of ω and ω').

Exercises. 1. A (non-constant) rational function cannot be periodic.

2. A (non-constant) single-valued analytic function cannot have 1 and $\sqrt{2}$ as periods.

3. As a supplement to the consideration of p. 61 for determining ω and ω', show that there can be at most two, four, or six periods on the circle (with center 0) on which ω lies. These are then at the ends of a diameter, the vertices of a rectangle, the vertices of a regular hexagon, respectively.

4. If precisely two periods (hence, ω and $-\omega$) lie on the circle referred to in Exercise 3, the selection of ω and ω' described in the text leads to values for which the *period-ratio* $\tau = \omega'/\omega$ satisfies the conditions:

$$|\tau| \geq 1, \qquad -\tfrac{1}{2} < \Re(\tau) \leq \tfrac{1}{2}.$$

These relations are still valid if four or six periods lie on that circle, provided that a suitable one of these periods is denoted by ω. Proof?

§8. Simply Periodic Functions

One can visualize the periodicity of a simply periodic function in the following manner: Through an arbitrary point c of L, e.g., the origin, draw any line L' which does

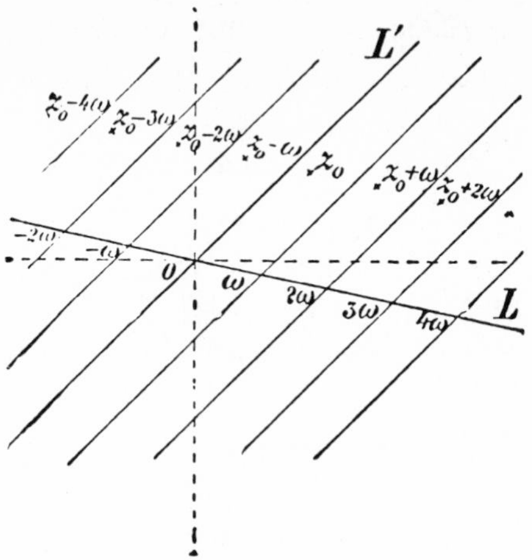

Fig. 4.

not coincide with L (see Fig. 4), and draw parallels to L' through all the points $c + n\omega$. The z-plane is thus divided into strips, which are called **period-strips.** The equation

$$f(z + n\omega) = f(z)$$

now means simply that the function $f(z)$ has the same values at "*congruent*" points, i.e., points that have congruent positions in pairs of strips[1] (cf. Fig. 4, where several points congruent to z_0 have been marked). Consequently, a periodic function exhausts its entire domain of values in one of the strips, even if one regards—as we shall always do in the sequel—only one of the two boundaries as belonging to the strip. In every other strip, all the values, and hence all regular and

[1]Two points z_0 and z_1 are called *congruent*, if their difference $z_1 - z_0$ is a period $n\omega$.

singular properties, occur once more: what holds for a point z_0 also holds for every other congruent point.

e^z has the primitive period $2\pi i$. L here is the axis of imaginaries, and for L' we can take the axis of reals. Then the region $0 \leq \Im(z) < 2\pi$, for example, is a period-strip. $\sin z$ has $\omega = 2\pi$ for a primitive period. Hence, if γ denotes any real number, the region $\gamma \leq \Re(z) < \gamma + 2\pi$ can be taken as a period-strip.

It is therefore sufficient to examine a simply periodic function in only one of the strips in order to get to know it completely. At the same time, it is useful to observe that it is no restriction to assume that ω has the particular value $+1$. For, if we set $z = \omega z'$, then $f(z) = f(\omega z')$ goes over into a function which, as a function of z', evidently has the primitive period $+1$.[1] Then precisely the *real integers* are the periods of the function, L is the axis of reals, and for L' we can now take the axis of imaginaries, so that the figure of the plane divided into period-strips becomes especially clear.

The nature of the function $f(z)$ is perceived more distinctly if we make use of the following artifice: We introduce a new variable ζ instead of z by setting

$$\text{(a)} \qquad z = \frac{1}{2\pi i} \log \zeta, \qquad \zeta = e^{2\pi i z},$$

and consider the function $\varphi(\zeta)$ defined by

$$f(z) = f\left(\frac{1}{2\pi i} \log \zeta\right) = \varphi(\zeta).$$

[1]In the foregoing, we have already written very often $e^{2\pi i z}$, $\sin 2\pi z$, $\cot \pi z$, etc. in order to make $+1$ a period of the function in question and thereby give the expansions a simpler form.

Since

$$f(z) = \varphi(\zeta) = \varphi(e^{2\pi i z}),$$

this can also be interpreted thus: The given periodic function will not be regarded or represented as a function of z itself, *but as a function of* $e^{2\pi i z}$.

Since $\log \zeta$ (cf. I, §26, 1) is an infinitely multiple-valued function, it would seem that $\varphi(\zeta)$ is also a multiple-valued function, and hence, that our investigation is rendered more difficult. However, due to the fact that all values of $\log \zeta$ result from a particular one by the addition of all integral multiples of $2\pi i$, all values of $\frac{1}{2\pi i} \log \zeta$ differ from one another by integral (real) numbers, and hence, only by periods of $f(z)$. The various determinations of $\log \zeta$ thus furnish *congruent* values of z, and $\varphi(\zeta)$ therefore proves to be a single-valued function. The multiple-valuedness of the logarithm is just compensated for by the periodicity of the function $f(z)$.

What is the region of existence of $\varphi(\zeta)$, and what is the nature of its singularities? Since $\log \zeta$ is singular at 0 and ∞ (but at no other point), these two points may be singular for $\varphi(\zeta)$. Other singularities, however, are not introduced by the function log. Apart from these two points, $\varphi(\zeta)$ can be singular in those, and only those, points ζ which, by virtue of (a), correspond to singular points z of $f(z)$. But now a considerable simplification takes place. For, if z_0 is singular for $f(z)$, so are all points of the form $z_0 + k$ with arbitrary integral $k \gtrless 0$. Only *one* singular point

$$\zeta_0 = e^{2\pi i z_0} = e^{2\pi i (z_0 + k)}$$

of the function $\varphi(\zeta)$ corresponds to this entire *set* of singular points of $f(z)$. $\varphi(\zeta)$ thus takes over, so to speak, the singularities of only *one* strip of $f(z)$.

We summarize this result in

Theorem 1. *Every one of the considered simply periodic functions $f(z)$ having the primitive period 1 can be regarded or represented as a single-valued function $\varphi(\zeta)$ of $\zeta = e^{2\pi iz}$. This new function is, in general, of a simpler nature than $f(z)$; for, by virtue of* (a), *only one singularity of $\varphi(\zeta)$ corresponds to every set of congruent singularities of $f(z)$. $\varphi(\zeta)$ is regular except for these and the possibly newly appearing singular points 0 and ∞.*[1]

Examples 1. For the sine-function we have, as is well known,

$$\sin 2\pi z = \frac{1}{2i}\left(e^{2\pi iz} - e^{-2\pi iz}\right) = \frac{1}{2i}\left(\zeta - \frac{1}{\zeta}\right).$$

$\varphi(\zeta)$ in this case is a very simple rational function.

2. Likewise, the rational function $\varphi(\zeta) = \frac{1}{2}\left(\zeta + \frac{1}{\zeta}\right)$ corresponds to the function $\cos 2\pi z$.

3. Similarly, we have

$$\tan \pi z = -i\,\frac{\zeta - 1}{\zeta + 1}, \qquad \cot \pi z = +i\,\frac{\zeta + 1}{\zeta - 1}.$$

(As it should, the *single* pole $\zeta = e^0 = +1$, for example, corresponds to the simple poles of the function $\cot \pi z$ at $0, \pm 1, \pm 2, \cdots$.)

With these agreements, it is now easy to derive a

[1]This result holds for every periodic function, and hence, also for the *doubly periodic* functions treated in the next paragraph.

form of expansion which is valid for all our functions $f(z)$. Since $f(z)$ is regular everywhere except for isolated singularities, one can in various ways, by means of parallels to the axis of reals, cut a rectangle out of the period-strip such that $f(z)$ is regular in its interior and on its vertical boundaries. If y_1 and y_2 ($> y_1$) are the ordinates of the aforementioned parallels, $f(z)$ is regular in the entire strip (P) which runs parallel to the axis of reals and is characterized by

$$y_1 < \mathfrak{J}(z) < y_2.$$

Consequently, $\varphi(\zeta)$ is regular provided that z in $\zeta = e^{2\pi i z}$ satisfies the condition just stated, i.e., provided that

$$e^{-2\pi y_2} = r_2 < |\zeta| < r_1 = e^{-2\pi y_1}.$$ [1]

Thus, $\varphi(\zeta)$ is single-valued and regular in an annulus determined by the rectangle which was cut out, and can therefore be expanded in one, and only one, Laurent series

$$\varphi(\zeta) = \sum_{n=-\infty}^{+\infty} a_n \zeta^n, \qquad (r_2 < |\zeta| < r_1),$$

in that ring. This series converges (see I, §30, p. 120) in the broadest ring that can be formed from the hitherto existing one by concentric contraction of the inner circle and expansion of the outer circle, and which is still devoid of singular points. If for ζ we substitute its value in terms of z, we obtain

Theorem 2. *Let $f(z)$ be a single-valued function with the primitive period 1. Then, to every strip (P) which is*

[1] $|e^{2\pi i z}| = |e^{2\pi i(x+iy)}| = e^{-2\pi y}$.

parallel to the axis of reals and is devoid of singular points, there corresponds one, and only one, expansion of the form

$$f(z) = \sum_{n=-\infty}^{+\infty} a_n e^{2n\pi iz}.$$

This series converges in the broadest strip that can be formed from (P) by a translation of its boundaries upward and downward, and which is still devoid of singular points. Outside this strip the series is divergent.

If this strip contains the axis of reals in its interior—which can always be brought about if the axis has no singular point on it,—we are led from this to the Fourier expansion of real analytic functions by substituting $e^{2\pi iz} = \cos 2\pi z + i \sin 2\pi z$. However, at this point we cannot enter further into this matter.

We must also be content to remark that from every other type of expansion of the single-valued function $\varphi(\zeta)$—ordinary power series, product expansion, partial-fractions expansion—we can, of course, derive a corresponding representation of $f(z)$ as a function of $e^{2\pi iz}$

Of the periodic functions, we have up to now met with only the elementary functions; we shall first get to know others in the next paragraph. For several we have obtained above (p. 68) the corresponding functions $\varphi(\zeta)$, which turned out to be particularly simple, namely: *rational.*[1] We conclude from this, that those simply periodic functions $f(z)$ for which the corresponding function $\varphi(\zeta)$ is rational are especially simple, but also especially important. Moreover, the class of these functions—*the class of rational functions of* $e^{2\pi iz}$—is

[1]The function ζ naturally corresponds to the exponential function itself.

governed by particularly beautiful and typical laws. We shall derive a few of these.

Theorem 3. *Every function $f(z)$ of this class possesses an algebraic addition-theorem; i.e., for variable z_1 and z_2, $f(z_1 + z_2)$ can be expressed algebraically in terms of $f(z_1)$ and $f(z_2)$.*

(For example, for the sine-function, if we make $+1$ the primitive period, we have the addition-theorem written in algebraic form:

$$\sin 2\pi(z_1 + z_2)$$
$$= \sin 2\pi z_1 \cdot \sqrt{1 - \sin^2 2\pi z_2} + \sin 2\pi z_2 \cdot \sqrt{1 - \sin^2 2\pi z_1}).$$

Proof: By hypothesis, $f(z) = R(\zeta)$, where R denotes a *rational* function of its argument. Consequently, if we set $e^{2\pi i z_1} = \zeta_1$, $e^{2\pi i z_2} = \zeta_2$, and hence $e^{2\pi i(z_1+z_2)} = \zeta_1\zeta_2$, we have

$$f(z_1) = R(\zeta_1), \quad f(z_2) = R(\zeta_2), \quad f(z_1 + z_2) = R(\zeta_1\zeta_2).$$

It is possible to eliminate ζ_1 and ζ_2 algebraically from these three rational equations in ζ_1 and ζ_2, so that the algebraic addition-theorem follows immediately.

Theorem 4. *Between any pair of functions $f_1(z)$ and $f_2(z)$ of our class, there exists an algebraic relation.*

Proof: From the hypothesis that

$$f_1(z) = R_1(\zeta) \quad \text{and} \quad f_2(z) = R_2(\zeta),$$

the assertion results immediately from the elimination of ζ.

With $f(z) = \varphi(\zeta)$, the function $f'(z)$, since it is equal to $2\pi i\zeta\varphi'(\zeta)$, also belongs to our class. If we apply the preceding theorem to this function, we obtain

Theorem 5. *Every function $w = f(z)$ of our class satisfies an algebraic differential equation of the simple form*[1]

$$w' = \frac{dw}{dz} = A(w),$$

where $A(w)$ denotes an algebraic function.

Since it follows from this—under suitable restriction of the variability of w—that

$$dz = \frac{dw}{A(w)}, \qquad z = \int_{w_0}^{w} \frac{dw}{A(w)} = F(w),$$

we can state finally:

Theorem 6. *Every such function $w = f(z)$ is the inverse of the integral $z = F(w)$ of an algebraic function.*[2]

Exercises. 1. Do there exist (single-valued) simply periodic functions having prescribed zeros (with prescribed orders) in the period-strip? If so, how are they to be set up explicitly?

2. Do there exist (single-valued) simply periodic functions having prescribed isolated singular points in the period-strip? For given principal parts, how can they be set up explicitly?

3. On what region in the w-plane does the function $w = e^{(2\pi i/\omega)z}$ map the fundamental parallelogram of a network of parallelograms in the z-plane determined by (ω, ω')?

[1]It is of the first order and does not contain the independent variable.

[2]The reader should verify all of these theorems, and carry out their proofs, with $e^{2\pi iz}$ and the trigonometric functions.

§9. Doubly Periodic Functions; in Particular, Elliptic Functions

The periodicity of a doubly periodic function $f(z)$ can be visualized in a manner analogous to the case of simply periodic functions. If ω and ω' are a pair of primitive periods of $f(z)$, we draw (cf. Fig. 1 or 3) parallels to L through all points $n'\omega'$, and parallels to L' through all points $n\omega$. The entire plane is hereby divided into a network of parallelograms whose lattice points are precisely the period-points $n\omega + n'\omega'$. Let us imagine *this network to be drawn, or any other resulting from an arbitrary translation of this one.* Then the double periodicity of the function evidently means that $f(z)$ assumes the same value, or exhibits the same singularity, at *congruent* points, i.e., now, at points having congruent positions (whose difference is therefore a period) in different parallelograms of the same network. Every one of these parallelograms (that is, every parallelogram with the vertices a, $a + \omega$, $a + \omega + \omega'$, $a + \omega'$; a arbitrary) is called a (indeed, also *the*) period-parallelogram of the function $f(z)$, and we say that $f(z)$ is a doubly periodic function belonging to this period-parallelogram.

In order to get to know such a doubly periodic function completely, it is therefore sufficient to study it "in the period-parallelogram"; e.g., in the so-called "fundamental parallelogram" with the vertices 0, ω, $\omega + \omega'$, ω'. Every regular or singular property which the function possesses at a point z_0 is also found at every one of a set of points $z_0 + n\omega + n'\omega'$, which form the lattice points of one of our parallelogram networks.

The following theorem immediately follows from this remark:

Theorem 1. *There exists no (non-constant) doubly periodic entire function.* **(First Liouville theorem.)**

Proof: As an entire function, $f(z)$ is bounded in every finite region. Consequently, a relation of the form $|f(z)| < K$, where K denotes a suitable constant, is valid for all the points of a period-parallelogram. But then $|f(z)| < K$ for all other points, and hence, in the entire plane. From this it follows, according to I, §28, 1, that $f(z)$ is a constant. We had excluded this trivial case, however.

Thus, a (non-constant) doubly periodic function has at least one singular point in the period-parallelogram. The doubly periodic functions are classified according to the nature of these singular points, which, of course, are the same for every parallelogram.

Definition. *A doubly periodic function which has no singularities other than poles*[1] *in the period-parallelogram, or in other words: a meromorphic doubly periodic function, is called an* **elliptic function** *belonging to this period-parallelogram.*

We shall further concern ourselves with only these functions in the following. First, we should be entitled to inquire whether such functions exist at all,[2] for we have not encountered any up to now. Since we shall see presently, however, that the function $\wp(z)$, constructed

[1]The number of poles in the period-parallelogram then is necessarily finite.

[2]Their discovery, which goes back to Abel and Jacobi, was a very important scientific event.

in §6, Example 2, is an example of a doubly periodic function, we shall not consider the existence question at this moment.

According to the definition, an elliptic function has but a finite number of poles in the period-parallelogram. If we wish to enumerate these, we must make suitable agreements regarding the attachment of the boundaries to the parallelogram. We stipulate that *only the vertex a and the two sides emanating from it, exclusive of their other terminal points, shall be considered as belonging to the period-parallelogram with the vertices a, $a + \omega$, $a + \omega + \omega'$, $a + \omega'$.* With this agreement, it is obvious that for every point of the plane there is always one, and only one, congruent point in an arbitrary one of the period-parallelograms.

It now has a unique meaning to speak of the poles of an elliptic function "in the period-parallelogram." On this we base the

Definition. *The sum of the orders of the poles of an elliptic function in the period-parallelogram is called the* **order** *of the elliptic function.*

The first Liouville theorem can then be stated also as follows:

Theorem 1a. *There exists no (non-constant) elliptic function of order zero.*

Immediately obvious is the following theorem for arbitrary doubly periodic functions:

Theorem 2. *The sum, difference, product, and quotient of two doubly periodic functions $f_1(z)$ and $f_2(z)$ with the pair of primitive periods (ω, ω'), as well as the derivative*

of such a function, are also periodic with the periods ω and ω'. (However, these do not necessarily constitute a pair of primitive periods for the new function; also, this function may be a constant.) If f_1 and f_2 are elliptic, so is the new function.

In connection with Theorem 1, this immediately leads further to

Theorem 3. *If two elliptic functions belonging to the same period-parallelogram have there the same poles with the same respective principal parts, then the functions differ by only an additive constant.*

For, their difference is an elliptic function of order zero.

There is the following important theorem concerning the residues at the poles:

Theorem 4. *The sum of the residues at the poles of an elliptic function in the period-parallelogram*[1] *is equal to zero.* **(Second Liouville theorem.)**

Proof: According to I, §33, the sum in question—apart from the factor $2\pi i$—is given by the integral $\int f(z)\, dz$ taken along the boundary of the parallelogram in the positive sense, provided that no pole lies on the boundary. If this should not be the case for a first choice of the period-parallelogram, it can always be realized at once by means of a sufficiently small translation (e.g., in the direction of a diagonal), which obviously does not have any influence on the present assertion. We may therefore assume that that condition is already

[1]As the proof will show, for this theorem to be valid it is not necessary that ω and ω' be a pair of *primitive* periods of $f(z)$.

Allen B. Altman

satisfied to begin with. If, then, a is the vertex associated with this parallelogram,

$$\int f(z)\,dz = \int_a^{a+\omega} f(z)\,dz + \int_{a+\omega}^{a+\omega+\omega'} f(z)\,dz + \int_{a+\omega+\omega'}^{a+\omega'} f(z)\,dz + \int_{a+\omega'}^{a} f(z)\,dz.$$

Now, we see immediately that the first and third integrals, as well as the second and fourth, differ only in sign; and hence, that their sum is zero. For if we replace z by $z + \omega'$ in the third integral, it becomes

$$\int_{a+\omega}^{a} f(z+\omega')\,dz = -\int_a^{a+\omega} f(z)\,dz,$$

which is minus the first. The proof for the second and fourth integrals is similar. Hence, the sum of the residues is zero, Q. E. D.

From this theorem follows

Theorem 5. *There exists no elliptic function of the first order.*

Proof: It could have only *one* pole of the first order in the period-parallelogram. If its residue were c, the sum of the residues there would also equal c. By the preceding theorem, we should have $c = 0$; i.e., such a pole cannot exist at all.

According to Theorem 2, with $f(z)$, the function $f'(z)/f(z)$ is also an elliptic function with the periods ω and ω'. If we apply Theorem 4 to this function, bearing in mind the proofs of I, §33, Theorems 2 and 3, we obtain

Theorem 6. *The number of zeros of an elliptic function in the period-parallelogram is equal to the number of its poles there—hence, equal to its order* **(Third Liouville theorem.)**

If we apply this theorem to $f(z) - a$, we obtain, finally, the following theorem, which completely settles the question as to the domain of values of an elliptic function:

Theorem 7. *In the period-parallelogram, an elliptic function of order m takes on every value, each precisely m times.*

After these general considerations, we now turn to the actual setting up of several elliptic functions, and the investigation of their most important properties. As we have already stated, the function $\wp(z)$, constructed in §6, Example 2, is an elliptic function. We first prove that this is true of its derivative. Since this derivative can be obtained by differentiating the series for $\wp(z)$ term by term, we have immediately

$$\wp'(z) = -\frac{2}{z^3} - 2\sum_{\nu=1}^{\infty} \frac{1}{(z - z_\nu)^3};$$

for which we can write, since z_0 was used to denote the origin,

$$\wp'(z) = -2\sum_{\nu=0}^{\infty} \frac{1}{(z - z_\nu)^3} = -2\sum_{k,k'} \frac{1}{(z - k\omega - k'\omega')^3},$$

where, in the last series, k and k' take on *all* integral values $\gtreqless$ 0 independently of each other and in any order. But if k runs over *all* the integers $\gtreqless$ 0, so does $(k - 1)$. Hence, if we substitute $z + \omega$ for z,

$$\wp'(z + \omega) = -2 \sum_{k,k'} \frac{1}{(z - (k - 1)\omega - k'\omega')^3}$$

is actually the same series. Consequently,

$$\wp'(z + \omega) = \wp'(z),$$

and in precisely the same manner we can show that

$$\wp'(z + \omega') = \wp'(z).$$

Herewith is proved the double periodicity of $\wp'(z)$, and hence, the existence of doubly periodic functions in general.

We can show still more precisely, that ω and ω' constitute a pair of *primitive* periods for $\wp'(z)$, and hence, that the numbers $z_\nu = k\omega + k'\omega'$ represent *all* of its periods. For, if Ω is any period of $\wp'(z)$, then $\wp'(z + \Omega) = \wp'(z)$ for every point of the domain of regularity of $\wp'(z)$. If we allow z to approach one of the lattice points, z_ν, (i.e., one of the poles of $\wp'(z)$), $\wp'(z)$ and therefore also $\wp'(z + \Omega)$ become infinitely large. Hence, $z_\nu + \Omega$, too, must be a pole of $\wp'(z)$, and consequently itself a lattice point, z_μ. According to this, $\Omega = z_\mu - z_\nu$, and so Ω is also of the form $k\omega + k'\omega'$, Q. E. D.

Now that we have this result, it is very easy to prove that $\wp(z)$ *itself is a doubly periodic function* with the same pair of primitive periods. By what we just proved, we have

$$\wp'(z + \omega) - \wp'(z) = 0,$$

and hence

$$\wp(z + \omega) - \wp(z) = c,$$

where c denotes a certain constant. We show that this constant must equal zero. The representation of $\wp(z)$ obtained in §6 implies, first of all, that $\wp(-z) = \wp(z)$ For, k and k' take on, independently of each other, all integral values in any order, without being zero simultaneously. We may therefore replace the letters k and k' by $-k$ and $-k'$, respectively. From this remark it follows (because of the exponent 2) that the series is not affected by changing z to $-z$. Hence, $\wp(z)$ is indeed an *even* function. If in $\wp(z + \omega) - \wp(z) = c$ we now substitute the value $z = -\frac{1}{2}\omega$, we obtain, as asserted, $\wp(\frac{1}{2}\omega) - \wp(-\frac{1}{2}\omega) = 0 = c$. Hence,

$$\wp(z + \omega) = \wp(z).$$

Since it is found, in an entirely similar manner, that

$$\wp(z + \omega') = \wp(z),$$

we have established the double periodicity of $\wp(z)$. That ω and ω' constitute a pair of *primitive* periods for this function too follows from the corresponding result for $\wp'(z)$ and from the fact that, in general,

$$\wp(z + \Omega) = \wp(z) \quad \text{implies} \quad \wp'(z + \Omega) = \wp'(z);$$

i.e., from the fact that $\wp'(z)$ can have no other periods than those of $\wp'(z)$. Since, finally, $\wp(z)$ and $\wp'(z)$ are meromorphic functions, we have, to sum up:

Theorem 8. *There exist doubly periodic functions; in particular, elliptic functions; and in fact, such functions* *possessing prescribed pairs of primitive periods. A first example thereof is furnished by Weierstrass's $\wp$-function.*

This $\wp$-function must, for diverse reasons, be regarded as the simplest elliptic function. For, since there exist no elliptic functions of order zero or one, only those of the second order come under consideration as the simplest. That one of these will be regarded as the simplest, which has precisely one pole—call it ζ—of the second order, with the simplest possible principal part, $1/(z - \zeta)^2$, in the period-parallelogram. If, in addition, this pole in the fundamental parallelogram lies at "the" vertex $\zeta = 0$, we are led directly to the function $\wp(z)$,—apart from only an additive constant which comes into question because of Theorem 3.

Even this constant—in itself unimportant—is most easy to determine: About every one of its poles, $\wp(z)$ can be expanded in a Laurent series. For a neighborhood of the origin, this series is of the form

$$\wp(z) = \frac{1}{z^2} + c_0 + c_2 z^2 + c_4 z^4 + \cdots . \text{[1]}$$

In this expression, the constant c_0 has the value zero, as we immediately infer from

$$\wp(z) - \frac{1}{z^2} = \sum_{\nu=1}^{\infty} \left[\frac{1}{(z - z_\nu)^2} - \frac{1}{z_\nu^2} \right]$$

for $z = 0$.

This "simplest" elliptic function plays a predominant

[1]Because the principal part is equal to $1/(z - \zeta)^2 = 1/z^2$, and, since $\wp(z)$ has already been shown to be an *even* function, no odd powers can appear.

role in the Weierstrassian theory of elliptic functions,[1] analogous to that of the exponential function in the theory of simply periodic functions. We can only illustrate this importance of the function $\wp(z)$ by means of several samples of the theory. We first prove (cf. §8, Theorem 5) the fundamental

Theorem 9. *The function $w = \wp(z)$ satisfies the algebraic differential equation of the first order:*

$$\left(\frac{dw}{dz}\right)^2 = (w')^2 = 4w^3 - g_2 w - g_3;$$

where g_2 and g_3 denote certain constants, the so-called "invariants of the $\wp$-function", which are determined by ω and ω' alone. The independent variable does not appear in the differential equation, and w' is an algebraic function of w.

Proof: From the series for $\wp(z) - z^{-2}$ which we just used, and setting[2]

$$\sum_{\nu=1}^{\infty} \frac{1}{z_\nu^n} = s_n$$

$(n \geq 3)$ for brevity, it follows, due to Weierstrass's double-series theorem (I, p. 83) and the fact that

$$\frac{1}{(z - z_\nu)^2} = \frac{1}{z_\nu^2} + 2\frac{z}{z_\nu^3} + 3\frac{z^2}{z_\nu^4} + \cdots,$$

[1]In the (older) Jacobian theory, a function plays the role of the simplest, which, in the period-parallelogram, has two separate poles with residues (then necessarily) differing only in sign. These poles lie at the midpoints of the sides belonging to the fundamental parallelogram.

[2]According to p. 29, the series are absolutely convergent for $n \geq 3$.

that

$$\wp(z) = \frac{1}{z^2} + 2s_3 z + 3s_4 z^2 + 4s_5 z^3 + 5s_6 z^4 + \cdots .$$

If, now, we follow Weierstrass and set

$$60s_4 = g_2 = 60 \sum_{k,k'}{}' \frac{1}{(k\omega + k'\omega')^4},$$

$$140s_6 = g_3 = 140 \sum_{k,k'}{}' \frac{1}{(k\omega + k'\omega')^6},$$

noting that the s_n with odd subscripts must equal zero,[1] then the initial terms of the desired expansion are

$$\wp(z) = \frac{1}{z^2} + \frac{g_2}{20} z^2 + \frac{g_3}{28} z^4 + \cdots$$

From this it follows, further, that

$$\wp'(z) = -\frac{2}{z^3} + \frac{g_2}{10} z + \frac{g_3}{7} z^3 + \cdots ,$$

$$(\wp(z))^3 = \frac{1}{z^6} + \frac{3}{20} g_2 \cdot \frac{1}{z^2} + \frac{3}{28} g_3 + \cdots$$

With these expansions, form the function

$$(\wp'(z))^2 - (4\wp^3(z) - g_2 \wp(z) - g_3).$$

According to Theorem 2, this function is, first of all, an elliptic function with the same periods and no other poles. It can be verified immediately, that no negative

[1]Since the lattice points of the network, taken in suitable pairs, differ only in sign, the corresponding pairs of terms of the series for s_n, with n odd, are annulled.

powers appear in its expansion for a neighborhood of the origin. Therefore, by Theorem 1a, the function reduces to a constant,—and in fact, to zero, since calculation shows further, that the constant term is also missing in the expansion. Hence, as asserted,

$$\wp'^2 = 4\wp^3 - g_2\wp - g_3,$$

where g_2, g_3 have the above-mentioned values.[1] It is well-known that, conversely, the function which satisfies such a differential equation is also uniquely determined as soon as two corresponding values of the

[1]This result has implications in many directions. We call attention at this point to the following:

By virtue of the equation

$$y^2 - (4x^3 - g_2x - g_3) = 0,$$

y is defined as a multiple-valued function of x, and x is defined as a multiple-valued function of y. (Here x and y, and afterwards t, denote complex numbers.) Each is an algebraic function of the other (further details of this are given in ch. 5); or, carrying over some notions from the "real" domain, we say that the equation defines an *algebraic curve*. Our foregoing result now shows that this "curve" has a parametric representation in

$$x = \wp(t),\ y = \wp'(t).$$

This fact, namely, that we have found two *single-valued* functions of a parameter t which yield precisely the same curve as the given implicit equation by means of which each of the variables x and y is defined as a *multiple-valued* function of the other, is expressed by saying that we have **uniformized** the curve. Thus, here we have uniformized a particular algebraic curve of the third degree with the aid of the $\wp$-function. We are dealing with a simpler case of uniformization when we represent the "circle" $x^2 + y^2 - 1 = 0$, with the aid of the trigonometric functions, in the form $x = \cos t$, $y = \sin t$. The problem of uniformization here indicated plays an important role in the modern theory of functions.

variables are known. For the $\wp$-function, $z = 0$ and $w = \infty$, e.g., constitute such a pair of values. Consequently, we infer from

$$\frac{dw}{dz} = \sqrt{4w^3 - g_2w - g_3},$$

that

$$z = \int_{\infty}^{w} \frac{dw}{\sqrt{4w^3 - g_2w - g_3}};$$

and hence, that $w = \wp(z)$ is the *inverse function*, or the *inverse*, of the function $z = z(w)$ defined by this integral.[1] Such an integral—more generally, every integral whose integrand is a rational function of the variable itself and of the square root of a polynomial in that variable of the third or fourth degree whose roots are all distinct—is called an **elliptic integral** (for the rather superficial reason that it first appeared in connection with the rectification of an arc of an ellipse). It was in the inverses of such functions defined by means of elliptic integrals, that Abel and Jacobi first discovered doubly periodic functions, which they therefore gave the name "elliptic functions".

[1]We started from the periods ω and ω', constructed the $\wp$-function belonging to these, and found the above-mentioned differential equation for this function, in which the invariants g_2 and g_3 were determined by ω and ω' alone. Now, the so-called *problem of inversion* is to determine whether, conversely, if g_2 and g_3 are assigned arbitrarily, the inverse of the function $z = z(w)$, given as the integral above, is a $\wp$-function whose invariants are the numbers g_2 and g_3.

We now set as our last aim, to prove a theorem which gives us, in a certain sense, a survey of the totality of elliptic functions:

Theorem 10. *Every elliptic function with the periods ω and ω' can be represented rationally in terms of the function $\wp(z \mid \frac{1}{2}\omega, \frac{1}{2}\omega')$ and its derivatives, provided that ω/ω' is not real.*[1]

The proof gives us at the same time an opportunity to become acquainted with several further important properties of our functions.

From $\wp(z + \omega) = \wp(z + \omega') = \wp(z)$ it follows (cf. p. 47) that

$$(1) \quad \frac{\sigma'}{\sigma}(z + \omega) = \frac{\sigma'}{\sigma}(z) + \eta; \quad \frac{\sigma'}{\sigma}(z + \omega') = \frac{\sigma'}{\sigma}(z) + \eta',$$

if η and η' denote suitable constants.[2] And from this we find, further, that

$$\sigma(z + \omega) = c \cdot e^{\eta z}\sigma(z), \quad \sigma(z + \omega') = c' \cdot e^{\eta' z}\sigma(z).$$

Since $\sigma(z)$ is also an odd function, the new constants are again obtained by letting $z = -\frac{1}{2}\omega$, and we have more precisely:

[1]That, conversely, every function which is a rational combination of $\wp(z)$ and its derivatives is an elliptic function with the periods ω and ω', is self-evident according to Theorem 2.

[2]Since $\frac{\sigma'}{\sigma}(z)$ is an odd function, we find, on setting $z = -\frac{1}{2}\omega$, that $\frac{1}{2}\eta = \frac{\sigma'}{\sigma}(\frac{1}{2}\omega)$. Hence, according to p. 46, η can be calculated by means of a series, and η', of course, likewise.

$$(2)\qquad \begin{cases}\sigma(z+\omega\,) = -e^{\eta(z+\frac{1}{2}\omega)}\sigma(z),\\ \sigma(z+\omega') = -e^{\eta'(z+\frac{1}{2}\omega')}\sigma(z).\end{cases}$$

By means of the same two integration steps, we get the initial terms of the Laurent expansions for a neighborhood of the origin from those for $\wp(z)$:

$$(3)\qquad \frac{\sigma'}{\sigma}(z) = \frac{1}{z} + b_3 z^3 + \cdots ,$$

$$(4)\qquad \sigma(z) = z + d_5 z^5 + \cdots ,$$

where we need not know the easily calculated coefficients b_3, d_5, and all the following ones.

Now we see on the basis of (2), that the function

$$-\frac{\sigma(z-a)\,\sigma(z+a)}{\sigma^2(z)\cdot\sigma^2(a)},$$

in which a is an arbitrary point distinct from the lattice points, admits the periods ω and ω'; and hence, since it has only the single pole $z = 0$ in the fundamental parallelogram, that it represents an elliptic function, $\varphi(z)$, belonging to this parallelogram. Since, now,

$$\sigma(z \pm a) = \pm\,\sigma(a) + \sigma'(a)\cdot z \pm \tfrac{1}{2}\sigma''(a)\cdot z^2 + \cdots ,$$

the beginning of the expansion of $\varphi(z)$ for a neighborhood of the origin reads

$$\varphi(z) = \frac{1}{z^2} + \frac{\sigma(a)\cdot\sigma''(a) - (\sigma'(a))^2}{\sigma^2(a)} + c_2 z^2 + \cdots$$

$$= \frac{1}{z^2} - \wp(a) + e_2 z^2 + \cdots \qquad \text{(see p. 47)},$$

where again we need not know the coefficients $e_2, \cdots$.

These first few terms show, however, that $\varphi(z) - \wp(z) + \wp(a)$ is the constant 0; for, it is an elliptic function of order zero, which vanishes for $z = 0$. If, in order to emphasize the freedom in the choice of a, we write z' instead of a, we have the fundamental formula

$$\wp(z) - \wp(z') = -\frac{\sigma(z - z')\,\sigma(z + z')}{\sigma^2(z)\cdot\sigma^2(z')}.$$

If we differentiate this formula logarithmically, first with respect to z, then with respect to z', and add, we find the so-called *addition-theorem for the function* $\frac{\sigma'}{\sigma}(z)$

$$\frac{\sigma'}{\sigma}(z + z') = \frac{\sigma'}{\sigma}(z) + \frac{\sigma'}{\sigma}(z') + \frac{1}{2}\,\frac{\wp'(z) - \wp'(z')}{\wp(z) - \wp(z')}.$$

From this we obtain the addition-theorem for the function $\wp(z)$ by differentiating once more with respect to z:

$$\wp(z + z') = \wp(z) - \frac{1}{2}\frac{\partial}{\partial z}\left(\frac{\wp'(z) - \wp'(z')}{\wp(z) - \wp(z')}\right).[1]$$

With these preliminaries, we are now in a position to prove Theorem 10 as follows:

[1] If we perform the differentiation and make use of the differential equation for $\wp(z)$—from which we get $\wp''(z) = 6\wp^2(z) - (g_2/2)$,—we can also write the addition-theorem in the form:

$$\wp(z + z') = \frac{[2\wp(z)\wp(z') - (g_2/2)][\wp(z) + \wp(z')] - g_3 - \wp'(z)\wp'(z')}{2[\wp(z) - \wp(z')]^2},$$

in which it is seen to be an *algebraic addition-theorem* (cf. §8, Theorem 3), because $\wp'(z)$ and $\wp'(z')$ are expressible algebraically in terms of $\wp(z)$ and $\wp(z')$.

Let the given elliptic function $f(z)$ have the k poles $\zeta_1, \zeta_2, \cdots, \zeta_k$ with the respective principal parts

$$h_\nu(z) = \frac{a_{-1}^{(\nu)}}{z - \zeta_\nu} + \cdots + \frac{a_{-\alpha_\nu}^{(\nu)}}{(z - \zeta_\nu)^{\alpha_\nu}}$$

in the period-parallelogram with the vertices 0, ω, $\omega + \omega'$, ω'. Now, since each of the functions

$$\frac{\sigma'}{\sigma}(z), \quad \wp(z), \quad -\frac{1}{2!}\wp'(z), \quad +\frac{1}{3!}\wp''(z), \cdots$$

has at the origin a pole with the simple principal part

$$\frac{1}{z}, \frac{1}{z^2}, \frac{1}{z^3}, \frac{1}{z^4}, \cdots,$$

respectively, we see at a glance, that the function

$$H_\nu(z) = a_{-1}^{(\nu)} \cdot \frac{\sigma'}{\sigma}(z - z_\nu) + a_{-2}^{(\nu)} \cdot \wp(z - \zeta_\nu) -$$

$$- \frac{a_{-3}^{(\nu)}}{2!}\wp'(z - \zeta_\nu) + \cdots + \frac{(-1)^{\alpha_\nu} a_{-\alpha_\nu}^{(\nu)}}{(\alpha_\nu - 1)!}\wp^{(\alpha_\nu - 2)}(z - \zeta_\nu)$$

is a meromorphic function which has a pole with the principal part $h_\nu(z)$ at ζ_ν.

According to the addition-theorem for the $\wp$-function, $\wp(z - \zeta_\nu)$, and hence also its derivatives, can be expressed rationally in terms of $\wp(z)$ and its derivatives. Consequently, bearing in mind the formulation of our theorem, and replacing $\wp(z)$, $\wp'(z)$, $\cdots$ for brevity by $\wp$, $\wp'$, $\cdots$, we can write more simply

$$H_\nu(z) = a_{-1}^{(\nu)} \cdot \frac{\sigma'}{\sigma}(z - \zeta_\nu) + R_\nu(\wp, \wp', \cdots),$$

where by R_ν we mean a rational function of its arguments. If we now add together the H_ν, ($\nu = 1, 2, \cdots, k$), the sum

$$a_{-1}^{(1)} \frac{\sigma'}{\sigma}(z - \zeta_1) + a_{-1}^{(2)} \cdot \frac{\sigma'}{\sigma}(z - \zeta_2) + \cdots + a_{-1}^{(k)} \cdot \frac{\sigma'}{\sigma}(z - \zeta_k)$$

appears. By virtue of the addition-theorem for $\frac{\sigma'}{\sigma}(z)$, this sum can be replaced by

$$(a_{-1}^{(1)} + a_{-1}^{(2)} + \cdots + a_{-1}^{(k)}) \frac{\sigma'}{\sigma}(z) - \left[a_{-1}^{(1)} \frac{\sigma'}{\sigma}(\zeta_1) + \cdots + a_{-1}^{(k)} \frac{\sigma'}{\sigma}(\zeta_k)\right] + \{\text{a rational function of } \wp(z) \text{ and } \wp'(z)\}.^{1}$$

By Theorem 4, the parenthesis is equal to zero; and since the bracket is constant, the sum in question is a rational function of $\wp$ and $\wp'$. We set it equal to $R_0(\wp, \wp')$, and now we have

$$H_1(z) + \cdots + H_k(z) = R_0(\wp, \wp') + \sum_{\nu=1}^{k} R_\nu(\wp, \wp', \cdots).$$

The sum of all the $H_\nu(z)$ is thus a rational function of $\wp(z)$ and its derivatives, and hence, in particular, an elliptic function (despite the individually *non*elliptic

[1]If one $\zeta_\nu = 0$, the corresponding term in the bracket is missing.

terms $\frac{\sigma'}{\sigma}(z - \zeta_\nu)!$). If we subtract it from $f(z)$, this function obviously loses all its poles, and therefore reduces to a constant, C_0, so that we obtain the representation

$$f(z) = C_0 + R_0(\wp, \wp') + \sum_{\nu=1}^{k} R_\nu(\wp, \wp', \cdots)$$
$$= R(\wp, \wp', \cdots),$$

which is our theorem.[1]

We shall have to be satisfied, within the limits of our little book, with these samples taken from the very extensive theory of elliptic functions.

Exercises. 1. If ω is positive and ω' is a positive pure imaginary, then the $\wp$-function $\wp(z \mid \frac{1}{2}\omega, \frac{1}{2}\omega')$ is *real* on the boundary of the fundamental parallelogram (which in this case is a rectangle). Proof?

2. Under the conditions of the preceding exercise, on what region of the w-plane does $w = \wp(z)$ map the fundamental rectangle?

3. In connection with the preceding exercise, effect the conformal representation of a given rectangle on the unit circle.

[1]From $\wp'^2 = 4\wp^3 - g_2\wp - g_3$ we get, by differentiating:
$\wp'' = 6\wp^2 - (g_2/2)$, and further:
$\wp''' = 12\wp\wp'$,
$\wp'''' = 12\wp'^2 + 12\wp\wp'' = 120\wp^3 - 18g_2\wp - 12g_3$,

etc. We see, in general, that *all* higher derivatives of $\wp(z)$ can be expressed as *polynomials* in $\wp(z)$ and $\wp'(z)$. If we make use of this result, we can sharpen Theorem 10 to the effect that **all** *elliptic functions can be expressed rationally in terms of $\wp(z)$ and $\wp'(z)$.*

4. Is $e^{\wp(z)}$ an elliptic function?

5. Carry out in detail the proof of the algebraic addition-theorem for the $\wp$-function as indicated in the footnote on p. 88.

6. Show that, in the fundamental parallelogram, $\wp'(z)$ has the simple zeros $\frac{1}{2}\omega$, $\frac{1}{2}(\omega + \omega')$, $\frac{1}{2}\omega'$,—and no others.

Section II

MULTIPLE-VALUED FUNCTIONS

CHAPTER 4

ROOT AND LOGARITHM

§10. Prefatory Remarks Concerning Multiple-valued Functions and Riemann Surfaces

We return now to the developments in I, ch. 8, particularly those of §24. There we saw how one can, in general, derive more and more new functional elements from a first such element, given, say, in the form of a power series, by means of analytic continuations—of which every single one is always absolutely unique and necessary,—and thereby enlarge the domain of existence of the function. We imagined this to proceed as far as possible. The complete analytic function resulting in this manner from one element was defined to be *single-valued*, when its behavior at every single particular point, z_0, is always the same, independent of the path along which one may reach it by analytic continuations; in other words, when every point, z_0, which has *once* belonged to the interior of a circle of convergence can never constitute an obstacle for *any* continuation, and when it is always made to correspond to the same functional value in the process of any continuation. Then all points of the z-plane are separated unambiguously into the regular and the nonregular, and to every regular point there is made to correspond one, and only one, functional value. The totality of regular points forms a region in the sense of I, §4, the *region of existence* of the function, whose points are the "bearers" of the functional values of the single-valued function $w = f(z)$.[1]

These functions are naturally easier to handle[2] than others, and we have therefore dealt with them up to now almost exclusively.

All this is altered when we have a *multiple-valued* function before us, in which case the above-mentioned condition is not fulfilled in the continuation process. Then it is possible for several distinct functional values to correspond, as a result of different continuations, to one and the same point, and one and the same point may actually prove to be regular in one continuation and singular in another. Provisionally, we imagine that with every z are associated *all* those functional values

[1]Imagine the functional values w to be written on, pinned to, or in some other way affixed to the proper point z of the region of existence.

It is often advantageous to add the poles to the region of existence and to make them bearers of the value ∞.

[2]Nevertheless, it need not (cf. the remark in I, pp. 93-94) be possible to obtain a single-valued function completely with the aid of a single expression, as was indeed the case with the entire and the meromorphic functions.

The region of existence may also have the most varied and complicated forms; for there is actually the following **Theorem:** *For every region* $\mathfrak{G}$ (see I, p. 18), *there are analytic functions having precisely the region* $\mathfrak{G}$ *for their region of existence, and hence are not continuable beyond* $\mathfrak{G}$ (see, e.g., L. Bieberbach, *Lehrbuch der Funktionentheorie*, vol. I, New York, 1945, pp. 295-296).

which it acquires in the course of all possible continuations; in addition, if occasion arises, the designation "singular" is applied to it if it proves to be singular in *any* continuation.

Let $w = F(z)$ be the functional configuration obtained in this way. Then the symbol $w = F(z)$, for a given z, no longer has a uniquely determined sense, but rather can have several (a finite or an infinite number of) meanings. Examples are $\sqrt{z}$ and $\log z$, which we have already treated somewhat more closely.

The *main question*, then, is, in general, the following—at first formulated quite loosely: *How does one keep the various determinations of a multiple-valued function apart, how does one bring order and insight into its domain of values*?

In definite individual cases this question will usually assume the following form: If a problem which by its nature must have a fully unique solution is solved with the aid of a multiple-valued function, *which of its determinations is the one to use*?

A few examples, in which we make use of the already somewhat familiar function log, will throw light on this formulation of the question and its difficulty.

1. Let (cf. p. 3, footnote) $H(z) = a_0 + a_1 z + \cdots$ be an entire function with no zeros; let b_0 be the principal value of the logarithm of $a_0 (\neq 0)$. Then, as we have seen, in virtue of the condition that $h(0)$ shall equal b_0, $h(z) = \log H(z)$ becomes a well-defined entire function. For every z, $h(z)$ is *one* logarithm of $H(z)$; e.g., $h(1)$ is *one* value of $\log \left(\sum_{n=0}^{\infty} a_n \right)$. *Which one is it?*

2. Let the non-zero complex numbers a and b be distinct, and let k be a path connecting them but not passing through the origin. Then $\int_{a\,k}^{b} \frac{dz}{z}$ is a definite complex number. Since $\frac{d}{dz} \log z = \frac{1}{z}$, it is contained among the infinitely many values of $\log b - \log a$. *Which one of these values is it?*

3. Let the single-valued function $f(z)$ be regular on, and in the interior of, the simple closed path C (cf. I, §33, Theorem 2), and let $f(z) \neq 0$ *along* C. Let a denote any point of C. Then, since $\frac{d}{dz}(\log f(z)) = \frac{f'(z)}{f(z)}$,

$$\frac{1}{2\pi i} \int_C \frac{f'(z)}{f(z)}\, dz = \frac{\log f(a) - \log f(a)}{2\pi i}$$

is certainly an integer $\gtreqless 0$. *What is its value?*

4. Finally, we wish to show that a point may be regular for some continuations, singular for others: $\sqrt{-2\pi i}$ has two values; we select a definite one of these and denote it by c_0. Then we see immediately, that there exists one, and only one, power series, $\sum c_n(z-1)^n$, which begins with c_0, converges in a neighborhood of $+1$, and for which

$$[c_0 + c_1(z-1) + \cdots]^2 = -2\pi i + (z-1) - \frac{(z-1)^2}{2} + \cdots\ ;$$

which, consequently, in a few words, represents a value of $\sqrt{\operatorname{Log} z - 2\pi i}$, where Log z denotes the principal value of log z. $z = +1$ is, of course, a *regular* point for this functional element. If we now imagine this element to be continued along, say, the unit circle in the positive sense—which is obviously possible,—then, on returning, the point $+1$ turns out to be *singular*; for, Log z has been increased by $2\pi i$, and $\sqrt{\operatorname{Log} z}$ is evidently not regular at $z = +1$ any more.[1]

We can now formulate the question somewhat more sharply in the following manner: Let $w = f_0(z)$ be a regular element, at $z = z_0$, of the multiple-valued function $w = F(z)$, and let it be continuable along the path k extending from z_0 to ζ. Then we land at ζ with a definite one of the functional values $F(\zeta)$. *Which one of these values is it?*

For the present we shall give merely a cursory presentation of the method for overcoming these difficulties. Only after we have examined several examples more closely in this and the next chapter shall we seek a general answer in the last chapter.

The functional element from which we proceed may be assumed to be a power series. We imagine its circle of convergence to be cut out of paper, and its points to be made bearers of the (unique) functional values of the element. If, now, we continue the initial element by

[1]Something similar actually occurs already in the domain of real numbers. $x^3 + y^3 - 3axy = 0$ represents the so-called folium of Descartes. y is triple-valued for all $0 < x < a\sqrt[3]{4}$. The upper two of the three arcs are singular at $x = a\sqrt[3]{4}$ (the differential quotient is ∞) and "are joined there"; the other arc remains regular.

means of a second power series, we also think of its circle of convergence as being cut out and pasted in the proper position on the first disk. (We hereby obtain a figure like that in I, p. 100, Fig. 7b.) The parts pasted together are bearers of the same functional values, and are accordingly counted henceforth as a single sheet covered *once* with values. If we succeed in carrying out another continuation, we paste the new disk on in an entirely similar manner, etc. Each new disk is pasted on the preceding one, from which it was obtained by means of (*eo ipso* single-valued) continuation, in the manner described.

Suppose that, after repeated continuation, we arrive with one of the new circles over old territory—i.e., over a circular disk not immediately preceding (cf. I, p. 103 and Fig. 8). Then, the new disk shall be pasted together with the old one when, and only when, both are bearers of the same functional values, or, only so far as both bear the same functional values.[1] If, however, they bear different functional values, let them overlap and remain disconnected. Then two sheets, which are bearers of different—but on each sheet fully unique—functional values, are superimposed on this part of the plane.

We always obey this rule in the future, and we imagine our procedure to be continued as long as possible. Then there results a surface-like configuration which covers the plane with several, in general actually

[1]If the function is single-valued, then the united circles gradually fill out the entire region of existence of the function precisely once; and the resulting sheet, together with its affixed functional values, represents the function completely.

infinitely many, "*sheets*," which can have the most varied forms, and can be joined together in the most varied manners.[1] It is called the **Riemann surface** of the multiple-valued function $w = F(z)$ defined by the initial element. The entire domain of values of $F(z)$ is spread out on it in a completely single-valued manner, to the extent that, on every sheet, every point is the bearer of one, and only one, value. (All possible free boundaries or boundary points of a sheet of this surface are singular for the continuations giving rise to the sheet in question; for details, see below.)

Only after we have illustrated these very general ideas by several transparent examples shall we be able to fully appreciate the advantage of this method of representation.

Note, finally, that it is of course immaterial whether we continue by means of circular disks or by means of any other regions—say in the manner described in I, p. 92—provided only that we adhere to the agreements we have made.

Exercises. 1. Is it possible for a multiple-valued function to have the same value at two superposed points of its Riemann surface? Can it have the same value at *all* points of a neighborhood of two such points?

2. What kind of function (single-valued or multiple-valued) is defined by each of the following formulas:

[1]In the course of pasting sheets together, it is sometimes necessary to join two sheets which are separated by others lying between them. We must imagine this to take place without cutting the intermediate sheets, without touching them, so to speak, in the process. This, of course, is impossible for concrete execution, but causes no difficulty for the purely mental construction which we are solely concerned with here.

a) $\sqrt{e^z}$ b) $\sqrt{\cos z}$, $\cos \sqrt{z}$; c) $\sqrt{1 - \sin^2 z}$;

d) $\sqrt{\wp(z)}$; e) $\sqrt{\wp(z) - \wp(\frac{1}{2}\omega)}$; *f*) $\log (e^z)$?

§11. The Riemann Surfaces for $\sqrt[p]{z}$ and log z

1. $w = \sqrt{z}$ can be regarded as the simplest multiple-valued function. We saw in I, §26, 2, that it is possible to continue the real function $\sqrt{x}$, defined and positive for $x > 0$, into the complex domain. For a neighborhood of $+1$, e.g., the continuation is effected by the binomial series

$$[1 + (z - 1)]^{\frac{1}{2}}$$

$$= 1 + \frac{1}{2}(z - 1) - \frac{1}{2 \cdot 4}(z - 1)^2$$

$$+ \frac{1 \cdot 3}{2 \cdot 4 \cdot 6}(z - 1)^3 - + \cdots$$

Proceeding from this element, we can carry out the continuation absolutely unhindered and in a fully unique manner so long as we avoid the negative axis of reals. With reference to the procedure, described in the preceding paragraph, for constructing the Riemann surface, this has the following significance: By joining domains, we can first of all fill out the entire plane which is cut only along the negative axis of reals, and make every one of its points the bearer of a single value of $\sqrt{z}$ which is *uniquely* determined by the initial element that was chosen. We say that, from the entire domain of values of $w = \sqrt{z}$ (where every $z \neq 0$ bears *two* values), we have extracted a *branch* which is regular in the region just mentioned.

Now, since the origin is the only finite singularity (concerning the point ∞, see p. 105), a further, analogous continuation across the edges of this domain is possible. However, if, e.g., we continue downward across the upper bank of the cut, we are no longer permitted to paste together. For, the parts of the region which project from the upper bank into the lower half-plane are now bearers of *different* functional values. These values, as we know, are the values already affixed there multiplied by the factor $e^{2\pi i/2} = -1$; i.e., the first values with opposite sign. The plane is thus covered a second time by these regional segments;[1] and since the origin is the only obstacle to continuation, this second cover-

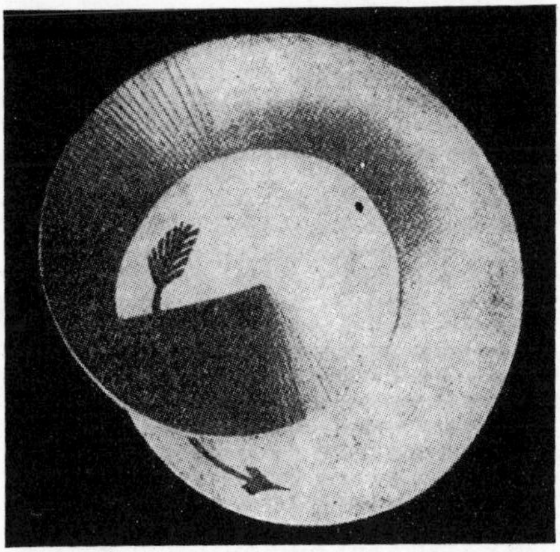

Fig. 5.

[1]We imagine this second sheet to lie *above* the first.

ing will eventually spread over the whole plane (excluding 0) until it returns to the negative axis of reals, receiving in the process the same values as before with sign changed.

Then the entire plane is overlaid with two sheets which wind around the origin, like a helicoid, in two turns, and on which the entire domain of values of $\sqrt{z}$ is spread out precisely once (cf. Fig. 5). The surface has two free boundaries, one above and one below, extending along the negative axis of reals, across which we can continue the function still further. Assume this to take place once more across the upper bank into the lower half-plane. Then, the attached regional parts, which at first cover the plane a third time, are bearers of values which again are equal to those below them multiplied by the factor (-1); they are thus bearers of the *same* functional values as those in the lower half-plane of the lowermost sheet. We therefore do *not* have a third sheet, but rather, in a few words, we must join the two free edges *by penetrating the intermediate sheet.* But then everything is accomplished at a blow. For now there is no free boundary and no possibility for an analytic continuation any more: we have obtained the *Riemann surface for the function* $w = \sqrt{z}$, on which the entire domain of values of this function is unfolded in a fully unique manner. $\sqrt{z}$ is a *single-valued* function of position on this surface. If we proceed from point to point along any path on the surface, we move in just as single-valued a domain of values as in the case of a single-valued function.[1]

[1]Since, after the first sheet was finished, we could have continued the function upward instead of downward, or in both direc-

A (non-zero) point of the surface now is no longer determined by z alone; it is also necessary to specify the sheet on which it lies. Since numbering the two sheets is, naturally, of no consequence, it is usually arranged so that the surface is thought of as being built up in some arbitrary, but henceforth fixed, manner. Then a point of the same is determined uniquely by naming z and the value of $\sqrt{z}$ affixed there. Finally, the point 0, round which the two sheets hang together, is also added to the surface, but is only counted *once*. We let it bear the value 0, and call it a *simple branch-point* of the surface (or a *branch-point of order one*). It is easy to verify that every complex number w is affixed once, and only once, to our Riemann surface.

In a neighborhood of every non-zero point of the Riemann surface, the attached domain of values constitutes a single-valued regular analytic function. Moreover, this neighborhood may be expanded so far as it remains single-sheeted and, consequently, does not contain the origin. If $\mathfrak{G}$ is such a region (e.g., the circle, in one sheet, with center z_0 and radius $|z_0|$; or the right half-plane of one sheet; or the plane cut along the

---

tions at the same time, we see that the form and position of the line of penetration of the two sheets is quite unimportant. The penetration is, so to speak, *not there at all*, or, in any case, is only involved in the imperfection of our empirical space-perception. Note, merely, that the winding-surface just has the characteristics that two sheets lie one above the other at *every* point distinct from zero, and that it is capable of returning us to any one of its points (different from zero), taken as starting-point, after a double circuit of the origin. The penetration of the intermediate sheet, which is necessary for our material spatial perception, need not be thought of at all; disregard it completely.

negative axis of reals), we say that it, together with its covering of values, represents a *branch* of the function.

(If, e.g., we denote by C the unit circle described in the positive sense, and if we begin at $+1$ with the meaning of $\sqrt{z}$ developed on p. 100, then accordingly

$$\int_{C\,+1}^{+1} \frac{dz}{\sqrt{z}} = [2\sqrt{z}\,]_{+1}^{+1(C)} = -2-2 = -4.)$$

2. Matters are analogous for the function $w = \sqrt[p]{z}$, $(p > 2)$. The results of I, §26, 2 show, on the basis of similar considerations, that in this case the continuation process, as it was envisaged with the aid of Fig. 5, is not yet complete after two encirclements of the origin. If we continue across the free edges of the surface obtained thus far (say, once more, across the upper bank into the lower half-plane), we see that a third covering of the plane is necessary in order to accommodate the domain of values; etc. Only after p coverings is it apparent[1] that another continuation across the upper bank into the lower half-plane does not lead to a new covering of the latter, but, rather, to the one which is already attached to the lowermost sheet in the lower half-plane. Therefore we penetrate the intermediate $(p - 1)$ sheets and fuse the upper bank of the pth sheet with the lower bank of the first sheet. Therewith every boundary disappears, and the continuation process is now complete.

[1]The values associated with the points of the second sheet differ from those of the first by the factor $e^{2\pi i/p}$, with those of the third, by the factor $e^{2(2\pi i/p)}$, $\cdots$, with those of the pth, by the factor $e^{(p-1)(2\pi i/p)}$, and, at the next step, differ by the factor $e^{p(2\pi i/p)} = 1$, i.e., *not at all*.

On this *p-sheeted Riemann surface for the function* $w = \sqrt[p]{z}$, its entire domain of values is uniquely unfolded, and, in addition, all the remarks we just made in the special case $p = 2$ are valid here. The origin is called a *branch-point of order* $(p - 1)$. We now add it to the surface, counting it *once*, and let it bear the value 0.

We indicate briefly, that it is possible to carry out exactly the same considerations using the *sphere* of complex numbers (cf. I, p. 4) instead of the z-plane. We arrive at an analogous two-, p-sheeted covering of the sphere with a *Riemann spherical surface*. The reader will be able to assure himself of this without any difficulty. The branch-point 0 of order $(p - 1)$ is now at the south pole, and we find—and herein lies the advantage of using the *sphere*—that the north pole, i.e., the point ∞, is a point of an entirely analogous nature, namely, a branch-point of order $(p - 1)$. We have before us a p-sheeted Riemann sphere with *two* branch-points; neither is favored above the other on the sphere. Corresponding to the agreements made in the case of 0, we also add the point ∞ to the surface, count it only *once*, however, and let it bear the value ∞.

It can be verified immediately, that *every* complex number w (including 0 and ∞) is affixed to the surface once, and only once.

One's insight into such a fact can be made more vivid in the following way: In studying a function $w = f(z)$, instead of letting the points z *bear* the values w, as we have done up to now, place near the z-plane (or z-sphere) a w-plane (w-sphere), and mark the *point* $w = f(z)$ on it. We call this point, briefly, the *image* of z in virtue of the mapping function $f(z)$. If we displace z

continuously on its sphere (naturally within the domain of existence of $f(z)$), w will also move continuously on its own sphere. Consequently, the mapping itself is said to be continuous. To every point, line, figure on the z-plane or z-sphere there corresponds, on the basis of this continuous representation, an "image" on the w-surface. The nature of this *mapping* must be regarded as *characteristic for the function.*[1]

If we make use of this notion, we can also state our last results as follows: *By means of* $w = \sqrt[p]{z}$, *the corresponding p-sheeted Riemann sphere is mapped one-to-one on the simple*[2] (*i.e., one-sheeted*) *w-sphere. To every point of the one configuration corresponds one, and only one, point of the other.*[3]

3. The construction of the Riemann surface for $w = \log z$ is analogous to that for $w = \sqrt[p]{z}$, since here, too, only 0 and ∞ are singular. We begin, say, with the principal value, regular at $+1$: the functional element

[1]We cannot discuss here in greater detail the *properties* of this mapping—its continuity was of course evident,—important as they are for the whole development of the theory of functions. Their investigation forms the content of the little volume of L. Bieberbach, *Einführung in die konforme Abbildung*, 3d ed., Sammlung Göschen No. 768, Berlin and Leipzig, 1937. See also C. Carathéodory, *Conformal Representation*, Cambridge Tracts No. 28, 1932.

[2]The German word is *schlicht*. The term "smooth" is sometimes used in this connection.

[3]If one imagines every point, z, of the z-plane to be connected with its image, w, of the w-plane by means of an invisible thread, then these, in their totality, constitute that "inner bond" of which we spoke in I, p. 103.

$$(z-1)-\frac{(z-1)^2}{2}+\frac{(z-1)^3}{3}-+\cdots.$$

It can (cf. I, §26, 1) be continued uniquely and unhindered over the z-plane cut along the negative axis of reals. We thus obtain a single-valued and regular function in this region; it is the *principal value* or *principal branch* of $\log z$.

We can further continue across the edges of the cut. If this is done, as in the case of $\sqrt[p]{z}$, we get a second sheet (to be thought of as lying *above* the first), whose points bear values equal to the subjacent ones increased by $2\pi i$. The same occurs when we come to a third sheet, etc. The construction of the surface proceeds in exactly the same manner as for $\sqrt[p]{z}$; except that here we never come to an end, because *every* sheet bears values equal to those immediately below increased by $2\pi i$. We therefore suppose that above *every* sheet there lies another one; whereby, in imagination, the continuation process in the upward direction is completed, i.e., a further extension in this direction is impossible.

Now, the lower bank of the first sheet is still free, and we can continue across it (into the upper half-plane). We think of the resulting new sheet as lying *below* the first; it bears values equal to the superjacent (principal) values diminished by $2\pi i$,—new values in any case. This ever-possible continuation process also produces new sheets with new coverings endlessly in the downward direction. For, every sheet bears values equal to those immediately above diminished by $2\pi i$. If we accordingly suppose that below *every* sheet there lies another, we finally, in imagination, complete the process of constructing the surface, which now is not open to extension in any direction.

The entire domain of values of $w = \log z$ is unfolded on this infinite-sheeted Riemann surface in a fully *unique* manner; $\log z$ is a *single-valued function of position* on the surface.

If we carry out the same procedure on the sphere instead of the plane—picture an infinite number of spherical shells wound around one another,—we see immediately that the point ∞ (the north pole) is exactly the same sort of point as the point 0. We have before us an *infinite-sheeted Riemann sphere with two branch-points of infinite order.* Such branch-points are *never* added to the surface, and are *never* made to bear functional values.

It remains for us to say a few words about the distribution of the domain of values of $\log z$ on our surface. On the first sheet are attached the principal values of $\log z = \int_1^z \frac{d\zeta}{\zeta}$, i.e., those for which the path of integration runs wholly—but arbitrarily—in the plane cut along the negative axis of reals. If, in order to get from $+1$ to z, we proceed, say, first along the positive axis of reals to the point $|z|$, and thence along the circle with center 0 and radius $|z|$ along the shortest path to z, we have

$$\log z = \int_1^{|z|} \frac{d\zeta}{\zeta} + \int_{|z|}^{z} \frac{d\zeta}{\zeta} = \int_1^{|z|} \frac{dx}{x} + i \int_0^{am\, z} d\varphi$$

$$= \operatorname{Log} |z| + i\, am\, z,$$

where $\operatorname{Log} |z|$ denotes the real logarithm of the positive number $|z|$, and we take

$$-\pi < \operatorname{am} z \leq +\pi.$$[1]

(The multiple-valuedness of $\log z$ accordingly appears as an immediate consequence of the ambiguity of the amplitude of a complex number.) The principal value of $w = \log z$ thus satisfies the condition

$$-\pi < \mathfrak{J}(w) \leq +\pi.$$

The *point* w therefore lies in the strip of the w-plane characterized by precisely this inequality; its width is 2π, and it lies symmetric with respect to the axis of reals. We read off from $z = e^w$, that *every* point w of this strip is the image of a $z \neq 0$. Consequently, by means of the principal value of $\log z$, the cut plane, 0 excluded, is mapped one-to-one on the indicated strip of the w-plane. The remaining values of $\log z$, which are to be found on the other sheets, differ from the principal value by only a term of the form $2k\pi i$ with integral $k \gtrless 0$. The corresponding *points* w consequently lie in the strips characterized by

$$(2k - 1)\pi < \mathfrak{J}(z) \leq (2k + 1)\pi,$$

$$(k = \pm 1, \pm 2, \cdots).$$

These are joined to the first strip in an unbroken sequence, and fill out the entire w-plane precisely once.[2]

[1]We add the upper bank ($\operatorname{am} z = +\pi$) of the cut to the cut plane in order that every $z \neq 0$ shall lie in it precisely once.

[2]Evidently they are simply the *period-strips* of the function e^w. Indeed, according to this, the multiple-valuedness of $w = \log z$, which consists solely in an arbitrary term of the form $2k\pi i$, is precisely the "inverse" phenomenon to the simple periodicity of the inverse function $z = e^w$, which has the primitive period $2\pi i$.

We may therefore say that *by means of* $w = \log z$, *the infinite-sheeted Riemann z-plane with the two branch-points* 0 *and* ∞ (*not belonging to it*) *is mapped one-to-one* (*and continuously*) *on the simple w-plane*; or, that every complex number ($\neq \infty$) is attached to one, and only one, point on the Riemann surface for $\log z$.

The questions raised as examples on pp. 95-96 are now easily answered:

1. $\log H(z)$ is uniquely defined as follows: The choice of $\log H(0)$ means that we begin at the point $H(0)$ of an arbitrarily chosen, but now fixed, sheet of the log-surface. Let us proceed from 0 along two paths, k_1 and k_2, to a point z_0. Then the value of the function H varies from $H(0)$ to $H(z_0)$ along two paths which, since $H(z) \neq 0$, can neither pass through, nor enclose, the point 0. Both, therefore, lead us on the log-surface to one and the same perfectly well-determined point of a perfectly well-determined sheet. There the functional value $\log H(z_0)$ stands uniquely affixed.

2. $\displaystyle\int_{a,\,k}^{b} \frac{dz}{z} = \log b - \log a$ is now to be understood as follows: Beginning at the point a on any sheet (i.e., choosing $\log a$ arbitrarily), we describe the path k *on the log-surface*. Since k must not pass through 0, it leads us to the point b of a perfectly well-determined sheet, and here the value of $\log b$, which alone comes into question, is uniquely attached.

3. Here, too, everything is determined uniquely if we follow the path described on the log-surface by $f(z)$ as z traverses the path C.

As a further application, we prove the following

Theorem. *Let the two functions $f(z)$ and $\varphi(z)$ be regular in the simply connected region $\mathfrak{G}$. Let the simple closed path C lie within $\mathfrak{G}$, and let*

$$f(z) \neq 0, \qquad |f(z)| > |\varphi(z)|$$

along C. Then the two functions $f(z)$ and $f(z) + \varphi(z)$ have the same number of zeros in the subregion of $\mathfrak{G}$ enclosed by C. **(Rouché's Theorem.)**

Proof: According to I, §33, Theorem 2, it is sufficient to show that

$$\int_C \left[\frac{f' + \varphi'}{f + \varphi} - \frac{f'}{f}\right] dz = \int_C \frac{(1 + (\varphi/f))'}{(1 + (\varphi/f))} dz = 0.$$

The last integral is equal to $[\log(1 + (\varphi/f))]^{(C)}$, i.e., the difference between the initial value and the terminal value of $\log(1+(\varphi/f))$ when C is traversed in the positive sense. But, when z describes the path C, the value of $1 + (\varphi/f)$ remains in the right half-plane (actually, inside the circle with center $+1$ and radius 1), because $|\varphi/f| < 1$. Since the (more precisely: *every*) logarithm is fully unique there, the above-mentioned difference must equal zero, Q. E. D.

Exercises. 1. Evaluate the integrals

$$\int_{1,\,k}^{i} \frac{dz}{\sqrt[v]{z}} \quad \text{and} \quad \int_{1,\,k}^{i} \log z\, dz,$$

where k denotes the first quadrant of the unit circle that lies on the first-covered sheet of the proper Riemann surface.

2. What values can the integral $\int_1^{z_0} \frac{dz}{\sqrt[p]{z}}$ have for an arbitrary path extending from a definite one of the (p distinct) points $+1$ to a definite one of the (p distinct) points $z_0 \neq 0$?

What values can the integral $\int_1^{z_0} \log z \, dz$ have for a corresponding interpretation?

3. Prove the fundamental theorem of algebra, with the aid of Rouché's theorem, by setting

$$\varphi(z) = a_0 + a_1 z + \cdots + a_{n-1} z^{n-1} \text{ and } f(z) = a_n z^n, \quad (a_n \neq 0),$$

and choosing for C a circle with a sufficiently large radius.

§12. The Riemann Surfaces for the Functions $w = \sqrt{(z - a_1)(z - a_2) \cdots (z - a_k)}$

The situation as regards the function $w = \sqrt{z - a}$ (a arbitrary) is quite analogous to the case $w = \sqrt{z}$; only, instead of the origin, the point a is the simple branch-point. For the sphere, the difference appears even more unessential, since now, as before, we obtain a two-sheeted Riemann sphere with two branch-points. The branch-point which previously lay at the south pole now lies at a—in all other respects the considerations of the preceding paragraph remain unaltered.

It is but a short step from this surface to the surface

for the function $w = \sqrt{(z - a_1)(z - a_2)}$, where a_1 and a_2 denote arbitrary, but distinct, complex numbers. We again obtain a two-sheeted Riemann sphere having simple branch-points at a_1 and a_2. The point ∞ is now like any other point distinct from a_1 and a_2; i.e., the two sheets pass by each other smoothly at ∞.

We shall derive all this once more, directly, according to the general considerations of §10:

$$w = \sqrt{(z - a_1)(z - a_2)}$$

is regular at all points distinct from a_1 and a_2. If z_0 is such a point, let $\sqrt{z_0 - a_1}$ and $\sqrt{z_0 - a_2}$ be arbitrary, but henceforth fixed, values of these double-valued square roots. Then, with the aid of the binomial series employed on p. 100, we obtain from the regular elements

$$f_\nu(z) = \sqrt{z_0 - a_\nu}\left(1 + \frac{z - z_0}{z_0 - a_\nu}\right)^{\frac{1}{2}}, \qquad (\nu = 1, 2),$$

at z_0 an expansion of w:

$$f = f_1 \cdot f_2 = c_0 + c_1(z - z_0) + c_2(z - z_0)^2 + \cdots,$$

which converges for a neighborhood of z_0. f constitutes an element of our function. Starting with this element, we shall construct the Riemann surface. We can continue unhindered over the entire plane so long as we avoid the points a_1 and a_2. Since $w = \sqrt{z - a_1} \cdot \sqrt{z - a_2}$, a multiple covering of a point z could only take place if it were reached along two paths beginning at z_0 and surrounding one of the two points a_ν. Let us cut the plane from a_1 to a_2 to ∞, and never pass over this cut during the continuation.[1] Then, by means of

[1]The cut can be drawn arbitrarily; but it must not intersect itself, and must avoid the point z_0.

our continuation process, one, and only one, functional value is associated with every point of this cut plane; the latter becomes a bearer of a branch of our function.[1] Now we can further continue across the banks of the cut, and the only question is, whether in so doing we obtain new coverings or not. If we had only the element $f_1(z)$ of the function $\sqrt{z - a_1}$ before us, we should only have to make one cut from a_1 to ∞ (corresponding to the cut along the negative axis of reals in §11), and, in crossing it, $\sqrt{z - a_1}$ would be multiplied by (-1). The same holds for the element $f_2(z)$ of the function $\sqrt{z - a_2}$ if we make a cut from a_2 to ∞. Accordingly, the cut from a_1 to a_2 to ∞ which we just drew can assume this role for both square roots. Let us continue across that part of the cut which extends from a_1 to a_2 (and which is oriented thus). Then, since f_1 goes over into $-f_1$ and f_2 remains unaltered, the regions already covered are overlaid with *new* values, namely, the old ones with sign changed. There results a second sheet—which we imagine to lie, say, *above* the first—with a second covering (differing from the first only in sign). It hangs together *crosswise*, to put it briefly, with the first sheet along the cut-segment in question, a crossing of this segment *always* leading us from one sheet to the other. The second sheet also must be thought of as being cut from a_2 to ∞.

Then *both* sheets at present are cut along $a_2 \cdots \infty$. If we cross this cut in the process of continuation still

[1]We are making use here of the following obvious **Theorem:** *If $f(z) = f_1(z) \cdot f_2(z)$ (identically) for the functional elements f, f_1, f_2, and if it is possible to continue f_1 and f_2, then the product of their continuations is a continuation of $f(z)$ itself.*

possible, *both* of the above-mentioned square roots are multiplied by (-1), so that w remains unaltered; i.e., such a crossing does *not* lead to a new covering, but we must rather join each sheet to itself along this part of the original cut. Therewith all boundaries disappear, and hence no further continuation is possible. Thus, we have obtained once more the above-described two-sheeted Riemann surface with two branch-points.

$\sqrt{(z-a_1)(z-a_2)}$ is a *single-valued* function of position on this surface. We again add the points a_1 and a_2 (each counted only *once*) to the surface and let them bear the value 0, and we likewise add the points ∞ of the two sheets (which are simple there) and let them bear the value ∞. Then *every* complex number w (including ∞) is to be found *at precisely two points* of our Riemann surface.

It is not at all difficult to apply these considerations to the functions

$$w = \sqrt{(z-a_1)(z-a_2)\cdots(z-a_k)},$$

where $k > 2$, and $a_1, a_2, \cdots, a_k$ are distinct, but otherwise arbitrary, complex numbers. One has only to draw a cut, not intersecting itself, from a_1 to a_2 to a_3 to $\cdots$ to ∞,[1] and carry out exactly the same considerations with the k factors $\sqrt{z-a_\nu}$, $(\nu = 1, 2, \cdots, k)$, into which our function can be factored, as we just did for $k = 1, 2$. We find, then, that the two sheets must be joined *crosswise* between a_1 and a_2, and likewise between a_3 and a_4, etc., whereas each sheet must be rejoined *to itself* between a_2 and a_3, a_4 and a_5, $\cdots$. We

[1]If it is advantageous, the numbering of the a_ν may be changed for this purpose.

thus obtain in *both* cases, whether k be odd or even ($2r - 1$ or $2r$, say), a two-sheeted Riemann surface with the even number, $2r$, of simple branch-points lying at the points a_ν and—for odd k—also at ∞.[1]

We call attention to the particularly important cases $k = 3$ and $k = 4$, each of which leads to a two-sheeted surface with *four* branch-points.

Although these surfaces may seem to be quite analogous to those with two branch-points that were obtained for $k = 1$ and $k = 2$, a fundamental difference between the two deserves to be stressed. The two-sheeted sphere with *two* branch-points can be mapped one-to-one and continuously on the *simple* sphere. It follows from this,—also from direct consideration,—that every simple closed curve *on the surface*[2] divides it into two pieces which are completely separated by this curve—as is also the case for the simple sphere. It is customary to express this by assigning the two surfaces the same *genus*; in the present instance, the *genus zero.*

The two-sheeted sphere with *four* branch-points (which is obtained for $k = 3$ and $k = 4$) is essentially different in this respect. Let us draw the curve C (see Fig. 6), enclosing a_1 and a_2 (but only these two branch-points), entirely in the upper sheet. Then we can still connect the two points z_0 and z_1 on the upper sheet, where z_0 and z_1 lie on opposite sides of C, by means of a path lying on the surface but not intersecting C. In

[1]For even k, on the other hand, ∞ is an ordinary point, i.e., both sheets are simple there, so that ∞ appears on the surface twice—as was described in detail for $k = 2$.

[2]That is, the curve extends from a point z_0 of some sheet back to the same point on the same sheet.

Fig. 6 we attempt to make this clear by representing the path in the lower sheet by an interrupted line, in the upper sheet by a continuous line; the cuts along which the sheets have been joined crosswise are dotted.[1] We therefore assign a different genus to this surface, namely, the *genus one*. In general, the surfaces with $2r$

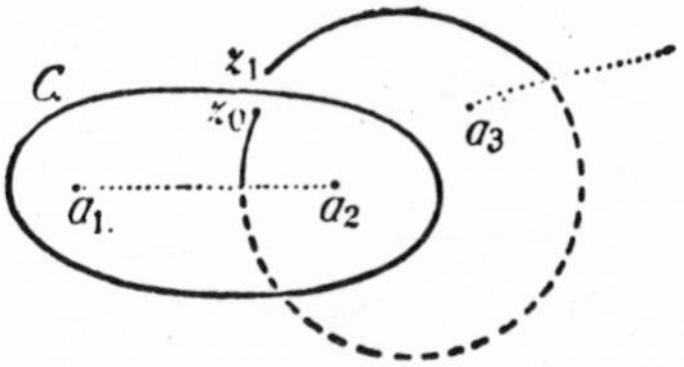

Fig. 6.

branch-points, corresponding to $k = 2r - 1$ and $k = 2r$, are given the *genus* $(r - 1)$.

We can only remark very briefly, that these essentially different connectivities of, e.g., the surfaces for $\sqrt{1 - w^2}$ and $\sqrt{4w^3 - g_2 w - g_3}$[2] constitute the basic reason that the integrals

$$z = \int_0^w \frac{dw}{\sqrt{1 - w^2}} \text{ and } z = \int_\infty^w \frac{dw}{\sqrt{4w^3 - g_2 w - g_3}}$$

[1]The cut beginning at a_3 leads to ∞ or a_4, according as k is equal to 3 or 4.

[2]Here we must interchange the letters z and w in order to remain in accord with §§8 and 9.

The above roots are, except for a constant factor, obviously of the type dealt with, with $k = 2$ and $k = 3$.

or, more clearly, their inverses

$$w = \sin z \quad \text{and} \quad w = \wp(z)$$

are of such fundamentally different types, namely, simply-, doubly-periodic, respectively.

Exercises. 1. Prove the theorem formulated in the footnote on p. 114.

2. What values can the integral $\int_0^{z_0} \frac{dz}{\sqrt{1 - z^2}}$ have if the path extends from a definite one of the two points 0, in an arbitrary manner, but avoiding the points ± 1, to a definite one of the points $z_0 (\neq \pm 1)$?

Do these integrals still have any meaning for $z_0 = \pm 1$ and $z_0 = \infty$? If so, what do they mean?

CHAPTER 5

ALGEBRAIC FUNCTIONS

§13. Statement of the Problem

All the examples of multiple-valued functions handled thus far, with the exception of log z, have been *algebraic functions*. They are named thus because they result from the solution of an algebraic equation, i.e., an equation of the form $G(z, w) = 0$, where G denotes an entire rational function of z and w. If we imagine G to be arranged in ascending powers of w, it can be written in the form

$$g_0(z) + g_1(z) \cdot w + g_2(z) \cdot w^2 + \cdots + g_m(z) \cdot w^m = 0,$$

where the coefficients $g_\nu(z)$ represent polynomials in z alone.

Now, if a functional element $w = f(z)$ is such, that when substituted for w in such an equation it satisfies the equation *identically*, i.e., that $G(z, f(z)) = 0$ for *all* z of a certain region, we say that $f(z)$ is an element of an *algebraic function* defined by $G(z, w) = 0$. If $m \leq 4$, one can solve the equation, and thereby obtain the function in question explicitly, and examine it. For $m > 4$ this is no longer possible, as is well known. There arises, then, just the problem of whether a function is *at all* defined in a similar manner by such an equation, whether only *one*[1] function is yielded, what the nature of this function is.

First we state the hypotheses precisely. We may assume $G(z, w) = 0$ to be *irreducible*, i.e., not expressible as the product of two polynomials of the same type as G.[2] For obviously the treatment of an equation of the form

$$G_1(z, w) \cdot G_2(z, w) = 0$$

can be replaced by the separate consideration of the equations $G_1 = 0$ and $G_2 = 0$.

If, now, we imagine a particular value z_0 to be substituted for z, we have before us an equation in w, with numerical coefficients, which, in general, will have m distinct roots $w_0^{(1)}, w_0^{(2)}, \cdots, w_0^{(m)}$. An exception takes place only if

a) $g_m(z_0) = 0$, because then the degree of the equation is lowered, or if

b) $G(z_0, w) = 0$ has multiple roots.

This last case can occur if, and only if, a certain expression, the so-called *discriminant* of the equation, which is an entire rational function of the coefficients, vanishes. Furthermore, if $G(z, w)$ is assumed to be irreducible, the discriminant, which we shall denote by $D(z)$, does not vanish identically, but, on the contrary, is a polynomial of a definite degree. (We must assume

[1]That more than one function may be defined by such an equation is already demonstrated by so simple an example as $w^2 - z^2 = 0$, which obviously yields *two* functions.

[2]This concept is an absolute one in the case of *two* variables, whereas in the case of *one* variable it has a definite meaning only after the nature of the numerical coefficients has been established.

that these algebraic facts are familiar to the reader.) Consequently, the exceptions mentioned under a) and b) can, in any case, occur *only for a finite number of special values of* z, which we denote by $a_1, a_2, \cdots, a_r$. We shall exclude these "critical points" from consideration for the present. Then we can say that the equation $G(z_0, w) = 0$ has precisely m distinct roots, $w_0^{(1)}, \cdots, w_0^{(m)}$, for every $z = z_0$ distinct from the critical points; z_0 is made the bearer of these roots. Our goal is the following

Theorem. *The m-fold domain of values, which is made to correspond to the points of the plane ("punctured" by the exclusion of the* a_ν*) in virtue of the equation* $G(z, w) = 0$, *is that of a single m-valued analytic function,* $w = F(z)$. *Or, more briefly: the equation* $G(z, w) = 0$ *defines precisely one m-valued regular function,* $w = F(z)$, *in the punctured plane.*

Functions that can be defined in such a manner are called **algebraic functions.**

We shall prove this theorem, which forms the basis of the theory of algebraic functions, in the next two paragraphs; and beyond that, we shall consider the behavior of $F(z)$ at the critical points, with which we also class the point ∞.

§14. The Analytic Character of the Roots in the Small

Let z_0 be a point which, for the present, is subject solely to the condition that $g_m(z_0) \neq 0$. Then $G(z_0, w) = 0$ has, in any case, m roots, some of which may be multiple roots, however. Let w_0 be such an α-fold root, $1 \leq \alpha \leq m$. Then there is the following

Theorem on the continuity of the roots. *If a circle K_ϵ with a sufficiently small radius $\epsilon > 0$ is described about w_0 as center, then it is possible to draw such a small circle K_δ with radius $\delta = \delta(\epsilon) > 0$ about z_0 as center, that, for every $z_1 \neq z_0$ in K_δ, the equation $G(z_1, w) = 0$ has precisely α distinct roots in K_ϵ.*[1]

Proof: If we set $w = (w - w_0) + w_0$ and arrange in ascending powers of $(w - w_0)$, we may write

$$G(z, w) = \bar{g}_0(z) + \bar{g}_1(z)\cdot(w - w_0) + \cdots + \bar{g}_m(z)\cdot(w - w_0)^m,$$

and for the new coefficients we have

$$\bar{g}_0(z_0) = \bar{g}_1(z_0) = \cdots = \bar{g}_{\alpha-1}(z_0) = 0, \; \bar{g}_\alpha(z_0) \neq 0.$$

Consequently, it is possible, first of all, to describe such a small circle $K_{\delta'}$ with radius $\delta' > 0$ about the point z_0 as center, that $D(z)$ and $\bar{g}_\alpha(z)$ differ from zero within and on the boundary of $K_{\delta'}$ (except, possibly, $D(z)$ at the center z_0, in case $\alpha > 1$). We then set

$$G(z, w) = \bar{g}_\alpha(z)\cdot(w - w_0)^\alpha\cdot[1 + A + B],$$

where

$$A = A(z, w) = \frac{\bar{g}_{\alpha+1}}{\bar{g}_\alpha}\cdot(w - w_0) + \cdots + \frac{\bar{g}_m}{\bar{g}_\alpha}\cdot(w - w_0)^{m-\alpha},$$

[1]This theorem, at the same time, gives a deeper interpretation of the multiplicity of a root; for it says that an α-fold root of an equation branches off into α simple roots if the coefficients of the equation are varied a little.

$$B = B(z, w)$$

$$= \frac{\bar{g}_{\alpha-1}}{\bar{g}_\alpha}\cdot\frac{1}{w - w_0} + \cdots + \frac{\bar{g}_0}{\bar{g}_\alpha}\cdot\frac{1}{(w - w_0)^\alpha}.^{1}$$

Now, let $c > 0$ be the greatest lower bound of $|\bar{g}_\alpha(z)|$ for all z in $K_{\delta'}$ (c is greater than zero because $\bar{g}_\alpha(z)$ vanishes neither inside $K_{\delta'}$ *nor on its boundary*), and let M be an upper bound for *all* $|\bar{g}_\nu(z)|$ in $K_{\delta'}$: $|\bar{g}_\nu(z)| < M$. Then, with $0 < \epsilon < \frac{1}{2}$ arbitrary to begin with, and for all z in $K_{\delta'}$ and all w within and on the boundary of the circle K_ϵ with center w_0 and radius ϵ, we have

$$|A| < \frac{M\cdot\epsilon}{c}(1 + \epsilon + \cdots + \epsilon^{m-\alpha-1}) < 2\frac{M}{c}\cdot\epsilon.$$

Now let ϵ be taken definitely less than $\frac{c}{4M}$, but otherwise arbitrarily, and let it remain fixed from now on. Then, for all z in $K_{\delta'}$ and all w in and on K_ϵ,

$$|A| = |A(z, w)| < \tfrac{1}{2}.$$

We now choose $0 < \delta < \delta'$ so small, that, in the interior of the circle K_δ with center z_0 and radius δ, the absolute values $|\bar{g}_0(z)|, |\bar{g}_1(z)|, \cdots, |\bar{g}_{\alpha-1}(z)|$ all remain less than the fixed number

$$\mu = \frac{c}{2\left(\frac{1}{\epsilon} + \frac{1}{\epsilon^2} + \cdots + \frac{1}{\epsilon^\alpha}\right)}.$$

[1]It is clear what is meant in the cases $\alpha = 1$ and $\alpha = m$.

(This is possible because all these coefficients vanish *at* the point z_0.) Then, for all z in K_δ and all w *on the boundary of* K_ϵ, i.e., for all z and w for which

$$|z - z_0| < \delta \quad \text{and} \quad |w - w_0| \overset{[sic!]}{=} \epsilon,$$

we have

$$|B| = |B(z, w)| < \mu \cdot \frac{1}{C}\left(\frac{1}{\epsilon} + \frac{1}{\epsilon^2} + \cdots + \frac{1}{\epsilon^\alpha}\right) = \frac{1}{2}.$$

We shall prove that our assertion is valid for these circles K_δ and K_ϵ. Let z_1 be an arbitrary point in K_δ. For all w *on the boundary* of K_ϵ,

$$|\bar{g}_\alpha(z_1)\cdot(w - w_0)^\alpha|$$
$$> |\bar{g}_\alpha(z_1)\cdot(w - w_0)^\alpha(A(z_1, w) + B(z_1, w))|,$$

because there both A and B in absolute value remain less than $\frac{1}{2}$. If we apply Rouché's theorem (cf. p. 111) to the functions of w(!) inside these absolute-value signs, and to the circumference of K_ϵ, we see immediately that $G(z_1, w)$ has precisely the same number of zeros in the *interior* of the circle K_ϵ as the function $\bar{g}_\alpha(z_1)\cdot$ $\cdot(w - w_0)^\alpha$ on the left does, i.e., *precisely* α *zeros*. And these must be distinct, because at z_1, which also lies in $K_{\delta'}$, $D(z_1) \neq 0$.

Now we make the further assumption that $D(z_0) \neq 0$, i.e., that $\alpha = 1$ at z_0. Then, for every $z = z_1$ in K_δ, there is *one, and only one,* root of $G(z_1, w) = 0$ in K_ϵ. Consequently, this root is a single-valued and continuous function, $f_1(z)$, of z, concerning which we have the

Theorem on the differentiability of the roots. $w = f_1(z)$ *is a regular function of* z *in* K_δ.

Proof: Let z_1 be an arbitrary point, and $z_1 + \zeta$ a neighboring point, both in the interior of K_δ. Let $f_1(z_1) = w_1$ and $f_1(z_1 + \zeta) = w_1 + \omega$, so that $G(z_1, w_1) = 0$, $G(z_1 + \zeta, w_1 + \omega) = 0$, and—because of the continuity of the function $f_1(z)$—as $\zeta \to 0$, $\omega \to 0$. Our new assertion then is simply that

$$\lim_{\zeta \to 0} \frac{f_1(z_1 + \zeta) - f_1(z_1)}{\zeta} = \lim_{\zeta \to 0} \frac{\omega}{\zeta}$$

exists. Now, if we arrange in ascending powers of ζ and ω, $G(z_1 + \zeta, w_1 + \omega) = G(z_1, w_1) + \zeta \cdot G_z(z_1, w_1) + \omega \cdot G_w(z_1, w_1) + \{$terms which contain at least the factors ζ^2, $\zeta\omega$, or $\omega^2\}$. Here $G_z(z_1, w_1)$ and $G_w(z_1, w_1)$ denote, as usual, the respective (partial) derivatives of $G(z, w)$ with respect to z, w alone, at (z_1, w_1). Since the left-hand side and the first term on the right are equal to zero, we can write

$$0 = \zeta[G_z(z_1, w_1) + P \cdot \zeta + Q \cdot \omega]$$

$$+ \omega\, [G_w(z_1, w_1) + R \cdot \omega],$$

where, for brevity, P, Q, R denote certain entire rational functions of ζ and ω. Here $G_w(z_1, w_1) \neq 0$, since w_1 was assumed to be a simple root of $G(z_1, w) = 0$; and we can therefore suppose ζ, and with it, ω, already so small, that

$$| R \cdot \omega | < | G_w(z_1, w_1) |.$$

But then the second bracket in the last equation is not zero; and it follows immediately that

$$f_1'(z_1) = \lim_{\zeta \to 0} \frac{\omega}{\zeta} \text{ exists and is equal to } -\frac{G_z(z_1, w_1)}{G_w(z_1, w_1)},$$

Q. E. D.

§15. The Algebraic Function

The theorems of the preceding paragraph have brought about the following situation: To every non-critical point z_0 of the plane, there correspond m distinct values, which can be combined in every sufficiently small circle about such a point—briefly: "in the small" —so as to form m separate single-valued and regular functional elements, which we shall denote by

$$f_1(z; z_0),\ f_2(z; z_0),\ \cdots,\ f_m(z, z_0).$$

These may be thought of as power series with center z_0.

We have now to show that all these elements belong to one and the same m-valued analytic function.

1. We see, first of all, that each one of the elements can be continued unhindered over the punctured plane. For, let K_0 be any circle in which one of our elements, say $f_1(z, z_0)$, is regular, and let z_1 be a non-critical boundary-point of K_0. Then,—because of the uniqueness of the combination in the small,—precisely one of the elements $f_\nu(z; z_1)$, $(\nu = 1, 2, \cdots, m)$, must coincide with $f_1(z, z_0)$ in that part of the neighborhood of z_1 which lies interior to K_0, wherewith the possibility of continuing f_1 is already demonstrated.

2. We now imagine the critical points $a_1, a_2, \cdots, a_r$ to be joined in any order, and then joined to the point

∞, by a simple line, L, composed of rectilinear segments and a half-line; and the plane to be cut along L (as in Fig. 7). Then each of the elements $f_\nu(z; z_0)$ can be continued unhindered over the cut plane—we shall denote this simply connected region by $\mathfrak{E}'$—so that, according to the monodromy theorem (cf. I, p. 105), each thus gives rise to a *single-valued* and *regular* function in $\mathfrak{E}'$. We shall denote the resulting functions by $F_1(z)$, $F_2(z)$, $\cdots$, $F_m(z)$, respectively. These functions, which are obviously independent of the choice of the starting-point z_0, combine "in the large" the entire m-fold domain of values borne by the points of $\mathfrak{E}'$ to form m separate single-valued and regular functions in $\mathfrak{E}'$; and, when substituted for w, satisfy the algebraic equation $G(z, w) = 0$ for every z in $\mathfrak{E}'$. All that remains to be shown, now, is that all these m functions can be continued into one another across the boundary, L, of $\mathfrak{E}'$—in a few words, that they are the m branches of one and the same analytic function. To this end we investigate

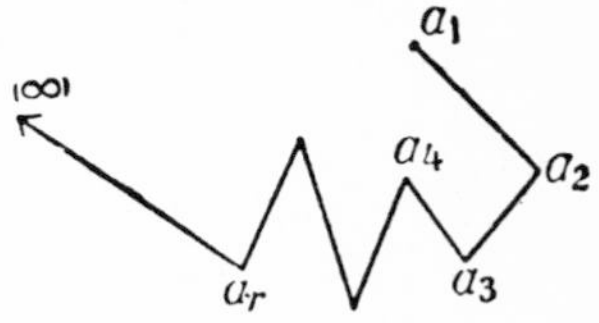

Fig. 7.

3. the behavior of the functions at the critical points and at ∞. Let a be one of the critical points; K, the circumference of a circle about a, which neither encloses nor contains any further critical points; z_0, a point of K. Then every one of the m elements $f_\nu(z; z_0)$ can be continued along K (say in the positive sense). On returning to the point z_0, each of these elements must—again because of the uniqueness of the combination of the domain of values in the small—be continued into a definite (but, in general, *different*) one of these,—and, of course, never two distinct elements into one and the same, since otherwise the inverse continuation would transform this last element into two distinct ones. To put it briefly, the m elements thus undergo a *permutation*. We suppose the elements to be numbered in such a manner, that the permutation carries f_1 into f_2, f_2 into $f_3, \cdots, f_{p-1}$ into f_p, and f_p back again into f_1, $(1 \leq p \leq m)$, so that the first p elements form a *cycle*.[1]

Then, in particular, $f_1(z; z_0)$, and with it, $F_1(z)$, goes over into itself after a p-fold continuation around a. If we accordingly set

$$(z - a) = (z')^p \quad \text{and} \quad F_1(z) = F_1(z'^p + a) = \varphi_1(z'),$$

$\varphi_1(z')$ is not only *regular*, but also *single-valued*, in a neighborhood of $z' = 0$, apart from this point itself. For, as the variable z' encircles the origin once (i.e., as its amplitude is increased continuously by 2π), z'^p encircles the origin, and hence z the point a, precisely p times, since the amplitude of $z - a$ is increased by $2p\pi$. Consequently, $\varphi_1(z')$ can be developed in a Laurent series,

$$\varphi_1(z') = \sum_{n=-\infty}^{+\infty} c_n z'^n,$$

[1]If, in a permutation of m objects, a subset of these undergoes a "*cyclic*" permutation, we say that the elements of this subset form a *cycle*. There is then the simple **Theorem**: *Every permutation can be expressed as the product of disjunct cycles.*

For example, let $m = 9$, and suppose that the figures 1, 2, 3, 4, 5, 6, 7, 8, 9 are transformed into 3, 7, 5, 4, 1, 8, 9, 6, 2, respectively. Then the figures 1, 3, 5, as well as 2, 7, 9, form a cycle of degree three; the figures 6, 8, a cycle of degree two; the figure 4 by itself, a cycle of degree one.

for a neighborhood of the origin, so that $F_1(z)$ admits of an expansion of the form

$$F_1(z) = \sum_{n=-\infty}^{+\infty} c_n \left(\sqrt[p]{z - a} \right)^n$$

for a neighborhood of the critical point a.[1] We now make the further assertion:

Only a finite number of negative powers appear in this expansion.

Proof: If $g_m(a) \neq 0$, so that $G(a, w) = 0$ has precisely m roots, some of which, however, are *multiple* roots, the theorem on the continuity of the roots states that these are continuous *at* the point a. Hence, in this case, *no* negative powers can appear in the above expansion.

But if $g_m = 0$, to the qth order, say, we must proceed otherwise. We can set $g_m(z) = (z - a)^q \cdot h_m(z)$, where $h_m(a) \neq 0$. Then, if we form

$$(z - a)^{q(m-1)} \cdot G(z, w),$$

one can verify immediately that, on setting $(z - a)^q \cdot w = v$, this can be written in the form

$$\Psi(z, v) = h_0(z) + h_1(z) \cdot v + \cdots + h_m(z) \cdot v^m,$$

where $h_0, h_1, \cdots, h_{m-1}$ denote suitable entire rational functions of z. Obviously the equation $\Psi(z, v) = 0$ is also irreducible, and, moreover, for *its* highest coefficient we have $h_m(a) \neq 0$. Hence, the roots of this new equation are continuous at $z = a$, and consequently,

[1]It is easy to verify that this one expansion represents all the p functions $F_1, F_2, \cdots, F_p$ of our cycle of degree p if we substitute for $\sqrt[p]{z - a}$ its p meanings. We shall not have to make use of this remark, however.

as in the case $g_m(a) \neq 0$ just treated, admit of an expansion of the form in question, in which, however, *no* negative powers appear. Since $w = (z - a)^{-q} \cdot v$, it follows immediately that the roots of the given equation, and hence our functions $F_\nu(z)$, also admit of an expansion of the same form in a neighborhood of the critical point $z = a$, and that *at most a finite number* of negative powers (namely, at most $p \cdot q$) can appear in this expansion, Q. E. D.

For the point $z = \infty$ the considerations proceed quite similarly; one has only to replace $z - a$ everywhere by $1/z$, and regard a sufficiently large circle as the circumference, K, surrounding the point ∞. These considerations, whose details everyone will be able to carry out for himself, show that each of the functions $F_\nu(z)$ admits of an expansion, for a neighborhood of the point ∞, of the form

$$\sum_{n=-\infty}^{+\infty} c_n \left(\sqrt[p]{\frac{1}{z}} \right)^n, \qquad (1 \leq p \leq m),$$

in which at most a finite number of negative powers of the pth root appear.

The critical points, with which we shall also class the point ∞, have thus been shown to be singularities of a particularly simple kind. We make the following

Definition. *If an analytic function is regular, though not necessarily single-valued, in a neighborhood of a point a or ∞,—apart from this point itself,—and if it admits of an expansion there of the form*

$$\sum_{n=-\infty}^{+\infty} c_n \left(\sqrt[p]{z - a} \right)^n, \qquad \sum_{n=-\infty}^{+\infty} c_n \left(\sqrt[p]{\frac{1}{z}} \right)^n,$$

respectively, in which only a finite number of negative powers of the pth root appear, then this point shall be called an algebraic point.[1] *We also say that the function has there the character of an algebraic function.*

4. We can now finally lay the keystone, and prove that every one of the m functions $F_\nu(z)$ can be continued into any other one by means of a suitable continuation across the cut, L.

For this purpose it is sufficient to show that F_1 can be continued into any other F_ν. For, if we can carry F_1 into F_ν and also into F_μ, then first, by the inverse continuation, F_ν is carried into F_1, and then further, in this indirect way, it passes from F_1 into F_μ; so that, in any case, F_ν can be continued into F_μ. Assume, now, that it is *impossible* to continue F_1 into some F_ν: suppose that these functions have been numbered so that F_1 can be carried into $F_2, F_3, \cdots, F_k, (k < m)$, but not into $F_{k+1}, \cdots, F_m$. This means, then, that by arbitrary continuation in the punctured plane, the first k functions are always permuted *among themselves* and are never carried into any of the remaining ones. If we form any *symmetric* function of them, $S(F_1, F_2, \cdots, F_k) = \Phi(z)$, it does not change at all, and is therefore single-valued and regular in the punctured plane. For a neighborhood of any critical point (including ∞), $\Phi(z)$ can be developed in an ordinary Laurent series having, according to **3.**, only a *finite number* of negative powers.

This means that $\Phi(z)$ has no singularities other than

[1]If $p = 1$, we are dealing with an ordinary *pole*; if, in addition to this, *no* negative powers appear, the point is actually regular. Naturally, we speak of an algebraic *singularity* only when this last is not the case.

poles in the entire plane (including ∞), and hence, according to I, §35, Theorem 2, it is a *rational* function of z. In particular,

$$(w - F_1)(w - F_2) \cdots (w - F_k)$$

$$= \varphi_0(z) + \varphi_1(z) \cdot w + \cdots + \varphi_k(z) \cdot w^k = 0$$

is an equation whose coefficients $\varphi_\lambda(z)$ are all *rational* functions of z. If we multiply this equation by a common denominator of the coefficients, there results an equation of the form

$$g(z, w) = \gamma_0(z) + \gamma_1(z) \cdot w + \cdots + \gamma_k(z) \cdot w^k = 0$$

with *entire rational* coefficients: an algebraic equation which is satisfied by the functions $F_1, F_2, \cdots, F_k$. But that is impossible for $k < m$ because of the assumed irreducibility of $G(z, w)$.[1] Our assumption is therefore untenable; and we have thus proved the theorem stated in the end of §13, and beyond that, the following

Theorem. *An algebraic function has no singularities other than algebraic singularities in the entire plane (including* ∞*).*

5. It is now an easy matter to construct the Riemann surface for the algebraic function defined by $G(z, w) = 0$. Corresponding to the m functions $F_\nu(z)$, we take m sheets, all cut along L, whose points bear the values of

[1]For, there is the purely algebraic **Theorem:** *If the equation* $g(z, w) = 0$ *has a root in common with the irreducible equation* $G(z, w) = 0$ *for all* z *of a region, then* $G(z, w)$ *is a factor of* $g(z, w)$*; and hence, the degree in* w *of* g *is at least as high as that of* G.

the functions $F_1, F_2, \cdots, F_m$, respectively. If we continue these functions one at a time across one of the segments of the cut, L, connecting two successive critical points, each of the F_ν goes over again into a definite one of these. We join the m sheets to one another in the manner hereby fully uniquely required,[1] whereupon this cut-segment disappears.

If we imagine the corresponding process to be carried out for *all* segments of the cut (including that which extends to ∞), *all* boundaries disappear, and the Riemann surface for the algebraic function defined by $G(z, w) = 0$ is complete. We see it more compactly, and the exceptional role of the point ∞ vanishes, if we start with the sphere instead of the plane. Then we have a closed m-sheeted Riemann sphere before us, every non-critical point of which is the bearer of one, and only one, functional value.

Finally, we shall make the critical points bearers of functional values, for which the following method suggests itself: By continuing around a critical point a (which may also be ∞), the m functions F_ν undergo, as we saw, a definite permutation, which can be decomposed into a certain number, say $l(1 \leq l \leq m)$ of disjunct cycles. Then, the point a shall be added to the surface, but counted only l (not m) times, *once* for all the sheets *together* that are connected in one and the same cycle. Every single one of these l superposed points a shall now be made bearer of the value c_0, ∞, according as *the expansion*, obtained in **3.**, *which corre-*

[1]Some sheets, in particular, may pass "smoothly" over the cut-segment,—if, namely, the function in question, F_ν, is carried into itself in crossing the cut.

sponds to it begins with the constant term c_0 or actually contains negative powers.[1]

Now that we have enlarged the domain of values in this manner, we call the totality of pairs of values (z, w), consisting of all points z of our Riemann sphere as first component, and the functional values w uniquely corresponding to these points as second component, the **algebraic configuration** *defined by* $G(z, w) = 0$. Its further, exhaustive investigation forms the subject of the theory of algebraic functions.

Exercise. Discuss in detail the structure of the Riemann surfaces (critical points; method of joining the sheets, and behavior of the function, at those points; distribution of the domain of values; etc.) for the algebraic functions, w, of z, defined by

a) $w^3 - 1 - z = 0,$

b) $w^3 - 3w - z = 0,$

c) $w + \dfrac{1}{w} - z = 0.$

[1]If the l cycles, in turn, are of degree $p_1, p_2, \cdots, p_l$, then exactly l branch-points, of order $p_1 - 1, p_2 - 1, \cdots, p_l - 1$, respectively, are superposed at a, (among which, in particular, branch-points of order zero, i.e., ordinary points, may also appear); and these, counted as l distinct points of the surface, may of course bear entirely different functional values.

CHAPTER 6

THE ANALYTIC CONFIGURATION

§16. The Monogenic Analytic Function

We are now in a position to supplement the definition of the complete analytic function which was given in I, pp. 102-103 but which still contains several omissions, and thereby give a certain completeness to our investigations, at least with respect to the fundamental idea—that of the analytic function. To this end we resume the considerations of §10.

We started there with a given functional element—say a power series—and continued it as long as possible. We must now indicate somewhat more precisely how this is to be carried out, be it only purely theoretically. For we shall require, in general, an infinite number of power series before a further continuation leads to nothing new. If, however, one is to give a constructive procedure according to which the continuation can be carried out in its entirety, it must consist of only an *enumerable number* of steps. This appears impossible at first, because it would seem that to exhaust the continuation possibilities of even only the first power series, one would have to form a new expansion about *every* point of its circle of convergence as center. But then there would be a *non-enumerable infinity* of new power series.

It is easy to see, however, that in a continuation

process—let us say the continuation of a power series $\mathfrak{P}_0$, with center z_0, along the path k to ζ—we need only use such new power series as have centers with *rational coordinates*.[1] For, if the continuation along k is at all possible, the requisite circles of convergence with centers $z_0, z_1, \cdots, z_{m-1}, z_m = \zeta$ (cf. I, p. 88 and Fig. 5) cover a region whose boundary is a positive distance, ρ, from k. If, now, we employ, instead of $z_1, z_2, \cdots$, any *rational* centers $z_1', z_2', \cdots$, each having a distance of at most $\frac{1}{2}\rho$ from k, we also arrive at ζ, and with the same functional element.

The rational points form an enumerable set, and from this we are able to infer that the entire continuation process for a functional element can be completed in an enumerable number of steps. For, only an enumerable number of new power series, say

$$\mathfrak{P}_{01}, \mathfrak{P}_{02}, \cdots, \mathfrak{P}_{0n}, \cdots,$$

result from the given power series $\mathfrak{P}_0$ if we make merely the rational points of its circle of convergence centers of the new expansions. At most an enumerable infinity arise again from each of these, so that we obtain, on the whole, only an enumerable number of *new* power series,[2] say

$$\mathfrak{P}_{11}, \mathfrak{P}_{12}, \cdots, \mathfrak{P}_{1n}, \cdots.$$

For these the argument repeats itself, etc.; so that we get all in all an enumerable number of sequences of

[1]For brevity we shall call such points *rational points.*

[2]That an enumerable set of enumerable sets of objects is itself an enumerable set of these objects was proved when we arranged the lattice points of the plane in a sequence; see p. 28.

enumerably many power series, and hence *all together an enumerable number of such series,* which we shall denote finally by

$$\mathfrak{P}_0, \mathfrak{P}_1, \mathfrak{P}_2, \cdots, \mathfrak{P}_r, \cdots .$$

This proves

Theorem 1. *If it is at all possible to include an arbitrary point z, by means of (power-series) continuation of the initial element $\mathfrak{P}_0$ along some path, in the interior of the circle of convergence of a new power series, it can be effected with the exclusive use of (in each case a finite number of) power series of a suitably fixed sequence $\mathfrak{P}_1, \mathfrak{P}_2, \cdots, \mathfrak{P}_r, \cdots$ of such.*

Suppose that we have exhausted in this manner all possibilities of continuing a given functional element $w = f(z)$. The result of this is that a neighborhood of every point z_0 of the plane which appears at all in the interior of one of the circles of convergence of the $\mathfrak{P}_r$ receives a finite or an enumerably infinite number of different coverings with functional values in such a manner, that every single covering forms a single-valued and regular function in a neighborhood of z_0. Let these be the functions

$$f_1(z; z_0), f_2(z; z_0), \cdots .$$

We then let the point z_0 bear the values of these functions for $z = z_0$; denote these values by $w_0^{(1)}, w_0^{(2)}, \cdots$. If the same value should appear more than once in this process, it shall be borne by z_0 correspondingly often. Finally, if we imagine the pairs of numbers

$$(z_0, w_0^{(1)}), (z_0, w_0^{(2)}), \cdots$$

to be formed for *every* z_0 belonging to the interior of at least one of the circles of convergence of the $\mathfrak{P}_r$, these pairs in their totality constitute the **monogenic analytic function** *generated by the initial element.* The function is thus determined by the following properties:

1. To every point z of the plane, or of a part of it, there correspond a finite or an enumerably infinite number of functional values $w^{(1)}$, $w^{(2)}$, $\cdots$ (among which the same ones may appear in an arbitrary manner).

2. If (z_0, w_0) is a particular one of these pairs of values, the *totality* of pairs (z, w), whose first component belongs to a neighborhood of z_0, can be combined so as to form a finite or an enumerably infinite number of regular functions $f_\nu(z, z_0)$ at z_0.

3. If $f_\nu(z; z_0)$ and $f_\mu(z; z_0)$ are an arbitrary pair of the functions thus formed, each is an (of course not *immediate*) continuation of the other.

4. If any one of these functional elements $f_\nu(z; z_0)$ is developed in a power series with a rational center, we obtain one of the power series $\mathfrak{P}_r$.

Accordingly, we can state, in particular, the following two theorems:

Theorem 2. *Every domain of values which is given in any manner "in the small"*[1] *generates, if at all, precisely one well-determined monogenic analytic function.*

Theorem 3. *The set of functional values which a*

[1] I.e., every covering of a region, however small, (or of a path segment, or of only a bounded infinite set of points) of the z-plane with w-values (cf. in this connection the considerations in I, p. 95).

multiple-valued function can assume at a point z_0 is either finite or enumerably infinite.

§17. The Riemann Surface

There is nothing now to prevent the construction of the Riemann surface belonging to a monogenic analytic function, according to the procedure indicated in §10: corresponding to the sequence of the $\mathfrak{P}_r$, we paste the disks of their circles of convergence together in the manner there described—penetrating (in imagination) intermediate sheets if necessary—and thus obtain the required surface.[1]

Naturally, the way in which the sheets are joined together *may* become very complicated. It *may* also, however, be very clear and transparent, as the examples treated in chapters 4 and 5 show. The Riemann surface lays no claim to being an end in itself, but is only intended as an aid to the imagination. One will therefore leave it aside in all those cases in which the joining of the sheets becomes so involved, that it would be more difficult to follow the functional values on the surface than with the function itself. Thus, the advantage of constructing, e.g., the surface for $w = \text{arc} \sin z$ in order to visualize the course of this function is no longer worth mentioning, although it would be very simple to set it up[2] on the basis of, say, the formula $w = \text{arc} \sin z$

[1]Instead of circular disks, we may, of course, take any other regions; in particular, such *maximal* regions in which a branch of the function remains regular. Thus, e.g., for the algebraic functions we could take the entire cut plane at once.

[2]It is nevertheless quite useful to construct these surfaces in imagination in order to get practice in using the ideas involved.

$= -i \log (iz + \sqrt{1 - z^2})$, which is obtained from $z = \sin w = -\frac{1}{2}i(e^{iw} - e^{-iw})$ by solving for w. But, e.g., in the case of the inverse of Weierstrass's σ- or $\wp$-function, the construction of the corresponding surface will offer hardly any advantage any more.

It is therefore not advisable to continue the formation of the Riemann surface in the most general instance. One should rather see from case to case whether its construction helps perception or not. We have become acquainted with the most important examples of useful surfaces in the preceding two chapters. As far as the general case is concerned, it is sufficient to know that, for a given function, a Riemann surface can be constructed at all events, on which its values form a *single-valued* function of position. Every point z is covered by as many (a finite or an infinite number of) sheets (see below) as there are different elements for a neighborhood of this point, and these sheets hang together in a perfectly definite manner. This last means that if we begin at a certain point z_0 of a particular sheet and describe any definite path (more precisely: a path whose projection on the ordinary z-plane is given), its course on the surface is fully unique, and consequently, leads us to a perfectly definite point of a perfectly definite sheet,—provided only that the path does not leave the surface, i.e., provided that it avoids the singular boundary points of those sheets (see below) on which it lies.

We are now finally in a position to formulate more precisely several concepts which we have already made much use of:

1. A **sheet** of the Riemann surface is obtained if,

starting with any one of our circular disks, we paste on new disks (or parts thereof), according to the above-described procedure, so long, but only so long, as we do not get a multiple covering of the plane. The concept of the sheet is thus, as we particularly emphasize, not an absolute one, but depends on the execution of the construction procedure just described. Nevertheless, it has a well-determined sense to speak of the different sheets on which a particular point z_0 lies: z_0 lies on as many different sheets as the number of times it is an interior point of distinct circular disks (i.e., disks not pasted together at z_0 and a neighborhood thereof). The totality of points z which belong to one and the same sheet form a region in the sense of I, §4.

2. By a **branch** of a given (multiple-valued) analytic function $F(z)$ we mean any function which is represented by the covering of *one sheet* of the proper Riemann surface, and which is single-valued and analytic in the region corresponding to it by 1.

3. By a **functional element** of an analytic function $F(z)$ we mean the representation of any branch or of only a part of it; in particular, each of the power series $\mathfrak{P}_r$, and each of the functions $f_\nu(z; z_0)$ used in §16,—for which, moreover, one can imagine the boundary of the neighborhood of z_0 which comes into question to be fixed in various ways,—is a functional element.

4. The concept of the **singular point** is, like that of the branch or the sheet, not an absolute one either: a particular point can be called singular or regular only for a certain branch or a certain sheet (cf. the example on p. 96). For this, however, the concept is fully determined. For, the region which, according to 1., is

filled by the totality of points z belonging to a sheet is covered with a domain of values which, by 2., forms there a single-valued analytic function—the branch belonging to this sheet. For this function the boundary points of the region in question are divided (cf. I, §24) unambiguously into regular and singular points, i.e., those at which the continuation across the boundary is possible, and those at which it is impossible, respectively.

Exercises. 1. Discuss in detail the structure of the Riemann surfaces for the functions

a) $w = z^a$ (a complex, arbitrary),

b) $w = \text{arc sin } z$.

(Cf. §15, ex. 2c.)

2. Construct a function for which the unit circle is the natural boundary, but which is

a) exactly two-valued, b) infinitely multiple-valued in the interior of the unit circle.

§18. The Analytic Configuration

We have yet to take up a last small supplement (similar to that which we made in the conclusion of §15 in the case of the algebraic functions), by means of which, then, the notion of a complete analytic function becomes settled in every respect.

The state of affairs thus far is the following: the domain of values which finds itself affixed to a neighborhood of an (*eo ipso: interior*) point of a sheet of the Riemann surface forms there a regular functional element, whereas all singular points of the separate branches (sheets) are, at first, not added to the surface at all. Among these singular points there are some of such a simple nature, that it is—also for various other reasons—advantageous to class them, so to speak, with the regular points, or, in any case, to add them to the surface. These are, in a few words, the algebraic singularities,—namely, the following points:

1. *The poles on a sheet*; i.e., every isolated boundary point z_0 of a sheet, such that the domain of values attached to a neighborhood of z_0 can be developed in an (ordinary) Laurent series with *only a finite number* of negative powers.[1] We let such a point bear the value ∞, and we add the pair (z_0, ∞) to the number pairs of the monogenic analytic function.

2. *The algebraic branch-points*; i.e., every singular boundary point of one of the sheets, about which a finite number, say $p(>1)$, distinct sheets hang together like the surface for $\sqrt[p]{z}$ at the origin, and for which the following condition is fulfilled: the domain of values affixed to these p sheets in a neighborhood of z_0, which (cf. p. 129) at all events can be developed in a series of the form

$$\sum_{n=-\infty}^{+\infty} c_n\left(\sqrt[p]{z - z_0}\right)^n,$$

shall be such, that no negative powers of $\sqrt[p]{z - z_0}$, or only a finite number of these, appear in this expansion.

We shall add such a point to the surface, and count it *once* for these p sheets *together*. We let it bear the value ∞ or c_0, according as negative powers do or do not appear in the expansion, and we add the pair

[1]On some other sheet, z_0 may very well be a regular point, or a different kind of singular point.

(z_0, ∞), (z_0, c_0), respectively, once to our pairs of numbers (z, w).

3. Finally, we shall add *the point* ∞ to the surface under corresponding conditions, namely, in a few words, if the behavior at the point ∞, *when regarded on the sphere,* is the same as that at the point z_0 in the cases just considered; in detail, if either

a) a certain sheet is simple in a neighborhood of the point ∞[1], and the domain of values attached to it there forms a single-valued regular function whose Laurent expansion about ∞ contains at most a finite number of negative powers of $\left(\frac{1}{z}\right)$;

or

b) a finite number, say $p(>1)$, of distinct sheets hang together about the point ∞ like the surface for $\sqrt[p]{z}$ about this point, and the (at all events possible) development of the affixed domain of values in the series

$$\sum_{n=-\infty}^{+\infty} c_n\left(\sqrt[p]{\frac{1}{z}}\right)^n$$

contains at most a *finite number* of negative powers of[2] $\sqrt[p]{\frac{1}{z}}$.

In case a) we say that there is an ordinary point, in case b), that there is a *branch-point of order* $p - 1$, at

[1]I.e., the sheet in question contains *all* points z which lie in the exterior of a certain circle.

[2]The cases 1 and 3a can, of course, be interpreted as the special cases of 2 and 3b obtained when $p = 1$.

the point ∞. It shall be added to the surface in both cases, and counted *precisely once* for the p sheets together that were taken into consideration. We let it bear the value ∞ or c_0, according as negative powers do or do not appear in the expansion in question. We accordingly add the pair (∞, ∞), (∞, c_0), respectively, once to our pairs of numbers.

We say, now, that the set of pairs (z, w), which has been supplemented in this way, represents **the (monogenic) analytic configuration** defined by the initial element.[1]

It is useful to add to the set of our functional elements $f_\nu(z; z_0)$ the finite or enumerably infinite number of expansions which we spoke of in 1. – 3. Then we have before us in the set of all these functional elements or in the set of all our pairs of numbers (z, w), completely and in clear arrangement, the *configuration* which arises, in the continuation process, from an arbitrarily given power series or other representation of a regular function in the small.

In conclusion let us add that the *theory of uniformization* mentioned on p. 84, footnote, is, in a way, the connecting link between the two main subjects of our

[1]Without proof we add the remark that, by interchanging the two components of every number pair of an analytic configuration (z, w) which arises from a functional element $w = f(z)$, there results another monogenic analytic configuration (w, z) which is designated as the *inverse configuration.* This transparent transition from an analytic function to its inverse could not be formulated so simply and clearly without the supplements met with in this paragraph. Their usefulness is already sufficiently assured by this fact alone.

investigation, the single-valued and the multiple-valued functions. For in it is proved the theorem that *any (multiple-valued) analytic function* $w = F(z)$ *can be completely represented (uniformized) with the aid of single-valued functions*; and this more precisely in the sense that there always exist two single-valued functions of the complex variable t, $z = z(t)$ and $w = w(t)$, with the property that the pair $(z, w) = (z(t), w(t))$ yields the complete analytic function $w = F(z)$ when the variable t runs over a certain domain of its plane. (General uniformization theorem of Poincaré and Koebe.)

BIBLIOGRAPHY

In addition to the works dealing with the general theory which were mentioned in *Theory of Functions, Part I*, we call attention to the following books relating to the more special classes of functions considered in the present volume:

P. Appell and É. Goursat, *Théorie des Fonctions Algébriques et de leurs Intégrales*, 2 vols., 2d edition, Paris, 1929-1930.

É. Borel, *Leçons sur les Fonctions Entières*, 2d edition, Paris, 1921.

———, *Leçons sur les Fonctions Méromorphes*, Paris, 1903.

H. Burkhardt, *Funktionentheoretische Vorlesungen*, vol. II, 3d edition, edited by G. Faber, Berlin, 1920.

H. Durège, *Theorie der elliptischen Funktionen*, 5th edition, revised by L. Maurer, Leipzig, 1908.

R. Fricke, *Die elliptischen Funktionen und ihre Anwendungen*, part I, Leipzig and Berlin, 1916, part II, Leipzig, 1922.

H. Hancock, *Lectures on the Theory of Elliptic Functions*, vol. I, New York, 1910.

K. Hensel and G. Landsberg, *Theorie der algebraischen Funktionen einer Variabeln und ihre Anwendung auf algebraische Kurven und Abelsche Integrale*, Leipzig, 1902.

C. Jordan, *Cours d'Analyse*, vol. II, 3d edition, Paris, 1913.

E. T. Whittaker and G. N. Watson, *A Course of Modern Analysis*, New York, 1945.

INDEX

CATALOG OF DOVER BOOKS

BOOKS EXPLAINING SCIENCE AND MATHEMATICS

THE COMMON SENSE OF THE EXACT SCIENCES, W. K. Clifford. Introduction by James Newman, edited by Karl Pearson. For 70 years this has been a guide to classical scientific and mathematical thought. Explains with unusual clarity basic concepts, such as extension of meaning of symbols, characteristics of surface boundaries, properties of plane figures, vectors, Cartesian method of determining position, etc. Long preface by Bertrand Russell. Bibliography of Clifford. Corrected, 130 diagrams redrawn. 249pp. 5⅜ x 8.
T61 Paperbound **$1.60**

SCIENCE THEORY AND MAN, Erwin Schrödinger. This is a complete and unabridged reissue of SCIENCE AND THE HUMAN TEMPERAMENT plus an additional essay: "What is an Elementary Particle?" Nobel Laureate Schrödinger discusses such topics as nature of scientific method, the nature of science, chance and determinism, science and society, conceptual models for physical entities, elementary particles and wave mechanics. Presentation is popular and may be followed by most people with little or no scientific training. "Fine practical preparation for a time when laws of nature, human institutions . . . are undergoing a critical examination without parallel," Waldemar Kaempffert, N. Y. TIMES. 192pp. 5⅜ x 8.
T428 Paperbound **$1.35**

PIONEERS OF SCIENCE, O. Lodge. Eminent scientist-expositor's authoritative, yet elementary survey of great scientific theories. Concentrating on individuals—Copernicus, Brahe, Kepler, Galileo, Descartes, Newton, Laplace, Herschel, Lord Kelvin, and other scientists—the author presents their discoveries in historical order adding biographical material on each man and full, specific explanations of their achievements. The clear and complete treatment of the post-Newtonian astronomers is a feature seldom found in other books on the subject. Index. 120 illustrations. xv + 404pp. 5⅜ x 8. T716 Paperbound **$1.50**

THE EVOLUTION OF SCIENTIFIC THOUGHT FROM NEWTON TO EINSTEIN, A. d'Abro. Einstein's special and general theories of relativity, with their historical implications, are analyzed in non-technical terms. Excellent accounts of the contributions of Newton, Riemann, Weyl, Planck, Eddington, Maxwell, Lorentz and others are treated in terms of space and time, equations of electromagnetics, finiteness of the universe, methodology of science. 21 diagrams. 482pp. 5⅜ x 8. T2 Paperound **$2.00**

THE RISE OF THE NEW PHYSICS, A. d'Abro. A half-million word exposition, formerly titled THE DECLINE OF MECHANISM, for readers not versed in higher mathematics. The only thorough explanation, in everyday language, of the central core of modern mathematical physical theory, treating both classical and modern theoretical physics, and presenting in terms almost anyone can understand the equivalent of 5 years of study of mathematical physics. Scientifically impeccable coverage of mathematical-physical thought from the Newtonian system up through the electronic theories of Dirac and Heisenberg and Fermi's statistics. Combines both history and exposition; provides a broad yet unified and detailed view, with constant comparison of classical and modern views on phenomena and theories. "A must for anyone doing serious study in the physical sciences," JOURNAL OF THE FRANKLIN INSTITUTE. "Extraordinary faculty . . . to explain ideas and theories of theoretical physics in the language of daily life," ISIS. First part of set covers philosophy of science, drawing upon the practice of Newton, Maxwell, Poincaré, Einstein, others, discussing modes of thought, experiment, interpretations of causality, etc. In the second part, 100 pages explain grammar and vocabulary of mathematics, with discussions of functions, groups, series, Fourier series, etc. The remainder is devoted to concrete, detailed coverage of both classical and quantum physics, explaining such topics as analytic mechanics, Hamilton's principle, wave theory of light, electromagnetic waves, groups of transformations, thermodynamics, phase rule, Brownian movement, kinetics, special relativity, Planck's original quantum theory, Bohr's atom, Zeeman effect, Broglie's wave mechanics, Heisenberg's uncertainty, Eigen-values, matrices, scores of other important topics. Discoveries and theories are covered for such men as Alembert, Born, Cantor, Debye, Euler, Foucault, Galois, Gauss, Hadamard, Kelvin, Kepler, Laplace, Maxwell, Pauli, Rayleigh, Volterra, Weyl, Young, more than 180 others. Indexed. 97 illustrations. ix + 982pp. 5⅜ x 8.
T3 Volume 1, Paperbound **$2.00**
T4 Volume 2, Paperbound **$2.00**

CONCERNING THE NATURE OF THINGS, Sir William Bragg. Christmas lectures delivered at the Royal Society by Nobel laureate. Why a spinning ball travels in a curved track; how uranium is transmuted to lead, etc. Partial contents: atoms, gases, liquids, crystals, metals, etc. No scientific background needed; wonderful for intelligent child. 32pp. of photos, 57 figures. xii + 232pp. 5⅜ x 8. T31 Paperbound **$1.35**

THE UNIVERSE OF LIGHT, Sir William Bragg. No scientific training needed to read Nobel Prize winner's expansion of his Royal Institute Christmas Lectures. Insight into nature of light, methods and philosophy of science. Explains lenses, reflection, color, resonance, polarization, x-rays, the spectrum, Newton's work with prisms, Huygens' with polarization, Crookes' with cathode ray, etc. Leads into clear statement of 2 major historical theories of light, corpuscle and wave. Dozens of experiments you can do. 199 illus., including 2 full-page color plates. 293pp. 5⅜ x 8. S538 Paperbound **$1.85**

PHYSICS, THE PIONEER SCIENCE, L. W. Taylor. First thorough text to place all important physical phenomena in cultural-historical framework; remains best work of its kind. Exposition of physical laws, theories developed chronologically, with great historical, illustrative experiments diagrammed, described, worked out mathematically. Excellent physics text for self-study as well as class work. Vol. 1: Heat, Sound: motion, acceleration, gravitation, conservation of energy, heat engines, rotation, heat, mechanical energy, etc. 211 illus. 407pp. 5⅜ x 8. Vol. 2: Light, Electricity: images, lenses, prisms, magnetism, Ohm's law, dynamos, telegraph, quantum theory, decline of mechanical view of nature, etc. Bibliography. 13 table appendix. Index. 551 illus. 2 color plates. 508pp. 5⅜ x 8.

Vol. 1 S565 Paperbound **$2.00**
Vol. 2 S566 Paperbound **$2.00**
The set **$4.00**

FROM EUCLID TO EDDINGTON: A STUDY OF THE CONCEPTIONS OF THE EXTERNAL WORLD, Sir Edmund Whittaker. A foremost British scientist traces the development of theories of natural philosophy from the western rediscovery of Euclid to Eddington, Einstein, Dirac, etc. The inadequacy of classical physics is contrasted with present day attempts to understand the physical world through relativity, non-Euclidean geometry, space curvature, wave mechanics, etc. 5 major divisions of examination: Space; Time and Movement; the Concepts of Classical Physics; the Concepts of Quantum Mechanics; the Eddington Universe. 212pp. 5⅜ x 8. T491 Paperbound **$1.35**

THE STORY OF ATOMIC THEORY AND ATOMIC ENERGY, J. G. Feinberg. Wider range of facts on physical theory, cultural implications, than any other similar source. Completely non-technical. Begins with first atomic theory, 600 B.C., goes through A-bomb, developments to 1959. Avogadro, Rutherford, Bohr, Einstein, radioactive decay, binding energy, radiation danger, future benefits of nuclear power, dozens of other topics, told in lively, related, informal manner. Particular stress on European atomic research. "Deserves special mention . . . authoritative," Saturday Review. Formerly "The Atom Story." New chapter to 1959. Index. 34 illustrations. 251pp. 5⅜ x 8. T625 Paperbound **$1.45**

THE STRANGE STORY OF THE QUANTUM, AN ACCOUNT FOR THE GENERAL READER OF THE GROWTH OF IDEAS UNDERLYING OUR PRESENT ATOMIC KNOWLEDGE, B. Hoffmann. Presents lucidly and expertly, with barest amount of mathematics, the problems and theories which led to modern quantum physics. Dr. Hoffmann begins with the closing years of the 19th century, when certain trifling discrepancies were noticed, and with illuminating analogies and examples takes you through the brilliant concepts of Planck, Einstein, Pauli, de Broglie, Bohr, Schroedinger, Heisenberg, Dirac, Sommerfeld, Feynman, etc. This edition includes a new, long postscript carrying the story through 1958. "Of the books attempting an account of the history and contents of our modern atomic physics which have come to my attention, this is the best," H. Margenau, Yale University, in "American Journal of Physics." 32 tables and line illustrations. Index. 275pp. 5⅜ x 8. T518 Paperbound **$1.45**

SPACE AND TIME, Emile Borel. An entirely non-technical introduction to relativity, by world-renowned mathematician, Sorbonne Professor. (Notes on basic mathematics are included separately.) This book has never been surpassed for insight, and extraordinary clarity of thought, as it presents scores of examples, analogies, arguments, illustrations, which explain such topics as: difficulties due to motion; gravitation a force of inertia; geodesic lines; wave-length and difference of phase; x-rays and crystal structure; the special theory of relativity; and much more. Indexes. 4 appendixes. 15 figures. xvi + 243pp. 5⅜ x 8.
T592 Paperbound **$1.45**

THE RESTLESS UNIVERSE, Max Born. New enlarged version of this remarkably readable account by a Nobel laureate. Moving from sub-atomic particles to universe, the author explains in very simple terms the latest theories of wave mechanics. Partial contents: air and its relatives, electrons & ions, waves & particles, electronic structure of the atom, nuclear physics. Nearly 1000 illustrations, including 7 animated sequences. 325pp. 6 x 9.
T412 Paperbound **$2.00**

SOAP SUBBLES, THEIR COLOURS AND THE FORCES WHICH MOULD THEM, C. V. Boys. Only complete edition, half again as much material as any other. Includes Boys' hints on performing his experiments, sources of supply. Dozens of lucid experiments show complexities of liquid films, surface tension, etc. Best treatment ever written. Introduction. 83 illustrations. Color plate. 202pp. 5⅜ x 8. T542 Paperbound **95¢**

SPINNING TOPS AND GYROSCOPIC MOTION, John Perry. Well-known classic of science still unsurpassed for lucid, accurate, delightful exposition. How quasi-rigidity is induced in flexible and fluid bodies by rapid motions; why gyrostat falls, top rises; nature and effect on climatic conditions of earth's precessional movement; effect of internal fluidity on rotating bodies, etc. Appendixes describe practical uses to which gyroscopes have been put in ships, compasses, monorail transportation. 62 figures. 128pp. 5⅜ x 8. T416 Paperbound **$1.00**

MATTER & LIGHT, THE NEW PHYSICS, L. de Broglie. Non-technical papers by a Nobel laureate explain electromagnetic theory, relativity, matter, light and radiation, wave mechanics, quantum physics, philosophy of science. Einstein, Planck, Bohr, others explained so easily that no mathematical training is needed for all but 2 of the 21 chapters. Unabridged. Index. 300pp. 5⅜ x 8. T35 Paperbound **$1.60**

A SURVEY OF PHYSICAL THEORY, Max Planck. One of the greatest scientists of all time, creator of the quantum revolution in physics, writes in non-technical terms of his own discoveries and those of other outstanding creators of modern physics. Planck wrote this book when science had just crossed the threshold of the new physics, and he communicates the excitement felt then as he discusses electromagnetic theories, statistical methods, evolution of the concept of light, a step-by-step description of how he developed his own momentous theory, and many more of the basic ideas behind modern physics. Formerly "A Survey of Physics." Bibliography. Index. 128pp. 5⅜ x 8. S650 Paperbound **$1.15**

THE NATURE OF LIGHT AND COLOUR IN THE OPEN AIR, M. Minnaert. Why is falling snow sometimes black? What causes mirages, the fata morgana, multiple suns and moons in the sky? How are shadows formed? Prof. Minnaert of the University of Utrecht answers these and similar questions in optics, light, colour, for non-specialists. Particularly valuable to nature, science students, painters, photographers. Translated by H. M. Kremer-Priest, K. Jay. 202 illustrations, including 42 photos. xvi + 362pp. 5⅜ x 8. T196 Paperbound **$1.95**

THE STORY OF X-RAYS FROM RONTGEN TO ISOTOPES, A. R. Bleich. Non-technical history of x-rays, their scientific explanation, their applications in medicine, industry, research, and art, and their effect on the individual and his descendants. Includes amusing early reactions to Röntgen's discovery, cancer therapy, detections of art and stamp forgeries, potential risks to patient and operator, etc. Illustrations show x-rays of flower structure, the gall bladder, gears with hidden defects, etc. Original Dover publication. Glossary. Bibliography. Index. 55 photos and figures. xiv + 186pp. 5⅜ x 8. T662 Paperbound **$1.35**

TEACH YOURSELF ELECTRICITY, C. W. Wilman. Electrical resistance, inductance, capacitance, magnets, chemical effects of current, alternating currents, generators and motors, transformers, rectifiers, much more. 230 questions, answers, worked examples. List of units. 115 illus. 194pp. 6⅞ x 4¼. Clothbound **$2.00**

TEACH YOURSELF HEAT ENGINES, E. De Ville. Measurement of heat, development of steam and internal combustion engines, efficiency of an engine, compression-ignition engines, production of steam, the ideal engine, much more. 318 exercises, answers, worked examples. Tables. 76 illus. 220pp. 6⅞ x 4¼. Clothbound **$2.00**

TEACH YOURSELF MECHANICS, P. Abbott. The lever, centre of gravity, parallelogram of force, friction, acceleration, Newton's laws of motion, machines, specific gravity, gas, liquid pressure, much more. 280 problems, solutions. Tables. 163 illus. 271pp. 6⅞ x 4¼. Clothbound **$2.00**

GREAT IDEAS OF MODERN MATHEMATICS: THEIR NATURE AND USE, Jagjit Singh. Reader with only high school math will understand main mathematical ideas of modern physics, astronomy, genetics, psychology, evolution, etc., better than many who use them as tools, but comprehend little of their basic structure. Author uses his wide knowledge of non-mathematical fields in brilliant exposition of differential equations, matrices, group theory, logic, statistics, problems of mathematical foundations, imaginary numbers, vectors, etc. Original publication. 2 appendixes. 2 indexes. 65 illustr. 322pp. 5⅜ x 8. S587 Paperbound **$1.55**

MATHEMATICS IN ACTION, O. G. Sutton. Everyone with a command of high school algebra will find this book one of the finest possible introductions to the application of mathematics to physical theory. Ballistics, numerical analysis, waves and wavelike phenomena, Fourier series, group concepts, fluid flow and aerodynamics, statistical measures, and meteorology are discussed with unusual clarity. Some calculus and differential equations theory is developed by the author for the reader's help in the more difficult sections. 88 figures. Index. viii + 236pp. 5⅜ x 8. T440 Clothbound **$3.50**

FREE! All you do is ask for it!

A DOVER SCIENCE SAMPLER, edited by George Barkin. 64-page book, sturdily bound, containing excerpts from over 20 Dover books explaining science. Edwin Hubble, George Sarton, Ernst Mach, A. d'Abro, Galileo, Newton, others, discussing island universes, scientific truth, biological phenomena, stability in bridges, etc. Copies limited, no more than 1 to a customer. FREE

THE FOURTH DIMENSION SIMPLY EXPLAINED, edited by H. P. Manning. 22 essays, originally Scientific American contest entries, that use a minimum of mathematics to explain aspects of 4-dimensional geometry: analogues to 3-dimensional space, 4-dimensional absurdities and curiosities (such as removing the contents of an egg without puncturing its shell), possible measurements and forms, etc. Introduction by the editor. Only book of its sort on a truly elementary level, excellent introduction to advanced works. 82 figures. 251pp. 5⅜ x 8. T711 Paperbound **$1.35**

FAMOUS BRIDGES OF THE WORLD, D. B. Steinman. An up-to-the-minute revised edition of a book that explains the fascinating drama of how the world's great bridges came to be built. The author, designer of the famed Mackinac bridge, discusses bridges from all periods and all parts of the world, explaining their various types of construction, and describing the problems their builders faced. Although primarily for youngsters, this cannot fail to interest readers of all ages. 48 illustrations in the text. 23 photographs. 99pp. 6⅛ x 9¼. T161 Paperbound **$1.00**

BRIDGES AND THEIR BUILDERS, David Steinman and Sara Ruth Watson. Engineers, historians, everyone who has ever been fascinated by great spans will find this book an endless source of information and interest. Dr. Steinman, recipient of the Louis Levy medal, was one of the great bridge architects and engineers of all time, and his analysis of the great bridges of history is both authoritative and easily followed. Greek and Roman bridges, medieval bridges, Oriental bridges, modern works such as the Brooklyn Bridge and the Golden Gate Bridge, and many others are described in terms of history, constructional principles, artistry, and function. All in all this book is the most comprehensive and accurate semipopular history of bridges in print in English. New, greatly revised, enlarged edition. 23 photographs, 26 line drawings. Index. xvii + 401pp. 5⅜ x 8. T431 Paperbound **$2.00**

FADS AND FALLACIES IN THE NAME OF SCIENCE, Martin Gardner. Examines various cults, quack systems, frauds, delusions which at various times have masqueraded as science. Accounts of hollow-earth fanatics like Symmes; Velikovsky and wandering planets; Hoerbiger; Bellamy and the theory of multiple moons; Charles Fort; dowsing, pseudoscientific methods for finding water, ores, oil. Sections on naturopathy, iridiagnosis, zone therapy, food fads, etc. Analytical accounts of Wilhelm Reich and orgone sex energy; L. Ron Hubbard and Dianetics; A. Korzybski and General Semantics; many others. Brought up to date to include Bridey Murphy, others. Not just a collection of anecdotes, but a fair, reasoned appraisal of eccentric theory. Formerly titled IN THE NAME OF SCIENCE. Preface. Index. x + 384pp. 5⅜ x 8. T394 Paperbound **$1.50**

See also: **A PHILOSOPHICAL ESSAY ON PROBABILITIES, P. de Laplace; ON MATHEMATICS AND MATHEMATICIANS, R. E. Moritz; AN ELEMENTARY SURVEY OF CELESTIAL MECHANICS, Y. Ryabov; THE SKY AND ITS MYSTERIES, E. A. Beet; THE REALM OF THE NEBULAE, E. Hubble; OUT OF THE SKY, H. H. Nininger; SATELLITES AND SCIENTIFIC RESEARCH, D. King-Hele; HEREDITY AND YOUR LIFE, A. M. Winchester; INSECTS AND INSECT LIFE, S. W. Frost; PRINCIPLES OF STRATIGRAPHY, A. W. Grabau; TEACH YOURSELF SERIES.**

HISTORY OF SCIENCE AND MATHEMATICS

DIALOGUES CONCERNING TWO NEW SCIENCES, Galileo Galilei. This classic of experimental science, mechanics, engineering, is as enjoyable as it is important. A great historical document giving insights into one of the world's most original thinkers, it is based on 30 years' experimentation. It offers a lively exposition of dynamics, elasticity, sound, ballistics, strength of materials, the scientific method. "Superior to everything else of mine," Galileo. Trans. by H. Crew, A. Salvio. 126 diagrams. Index. xxi + 288pp. 5⅜ x 8.
S99 Paperbound **$1.65**

A DIDEROT PICTORIAL ENCYCLOPEDIA OF TRADES AND INDUSTRY, Manufacturing and the Technical Arts in Plates Selected from "L'Encyclopédie ou Dictionnaire Raisonné des Sciences, des Arts, et des Métiers" of Denis Diderot. Edited with text by C. Gillispie. This first modern selection of plates from the high point of 18th century French engraving is a storehouse of valuable technological information to the historian of arts and science. Over 2000 illustrations on 485 full page plates, most of them original size, show the trades and industries of a fascinating era in such great detail that the processes and shops might very well be reconstructed from them. The plates teem with life, with men, women, and children performing all of the thousands of operations necessary to the trades before and during the early stages of the industrial revolution. Plates are in sequence, and show general operations, closeups of difficult operations, and details of complex machinery. Such important and interesting trades and industries are illustrated as sowing, harvesting, beekeeping, cheesemaking, operating windmills, milling flour, charcoal burning, tobacco processing, indigo, fishing, arts of war, salt extraction, mining, smelting, casting iron, steel, extracting mercury, zinc, sulphur, copper, etc., slating, tinning, silverplating, gilding, making gunpowder, cannons, bells, shoeing horses, tanning, papermaking, printing, dyeing, and more than 40 other categories. Professor Gillispie, of Princeton, supplies a full commentary on all the plates, identifying operations, tools, processes, etc. This material, presented in a lively and lucid fashion, is of great interest to the reader interested in history of science and technology. Heavy library cloth. 920pp. 9 x 12. T421 Two volume set **$18.50**

DE MAGNETE, William Gilbert. This classic work on magnetism founded a new science. Gilbert was the first to use the word "electricity", to recognize mass as distinct from weight, to discover the effect of heat on magnetic bodies; invent an electroscope, differentiate between static electricity and magnetism, conceive of the earth as a magnet. Written by the first great experimental scientist, this lively work is valuable not only as an historical landmark, but as the delightfully easy to follow record of a perpetually searching, ingenious mind. Translated by P. F. Mottelay. 25 page biographical memoir. 90 figures. lix + 368pp. 5⅜ x 8. S470 Paperbound **$2.00**

A CONCISE HISTORY OF MATHEMATICS, D. Struik. Lucid study of development of mathematical ideas, techniques from Ancient Near East, Greece, Islamic science, Middle Ages, Renaissance, modern times. Important mathematicians are described in detail. Treatment is not anecdotal, but analytical development of ideas. "Rich in content, thoughtful in interpretation," U.S. QUARTERLY BOOKLIST. Non-technical; no mathematical training needed. Index. 60 illustrations, including Egyptian papyri, Greek mss., portraits of 31 eminent mathematicians. Bibliography. 2nd edition. xix + 299pp. 5⅜ x 8. T255 Paperbound **$1.75**

See also: **NON-EUCLIDEAN GEOMETRY, R. Bonola; THEORY OF DETERMINANTS IN HISTORICAL ORDER OF DEVELOPMENT, T. Muir; HISTORY OF THE THEORY OF ELASTICITY AND STRENGTH OF MATERIALS, I. Todhunter and K. Pearson; A SHORT HISTORY OF ASTRONOMY, A. Berry; CLASSICS OF SCIENCE.**

PHILOSOPHY OF SCIENCE AND MATHEMATICS

FOUNDATIONS OF SCIENCE: THE PHILOSOPHY OF THEORY AND EXPERIMENT, N. R. Campbell. A critique of the most fundamental concepts of science in general and physics in particular. Examines why certain propositions are accepted without question, demarcates science from philosophy, clarifies the understanding of the tools of science. Part One analyzes the presuppositions of scientific thought: existence of the material world, nature of scientific laws, multiplication of probabilities, etc.: Part Two covers the nature of experiment and the application of mathematics: conditions for measurement, relations between numerical laws and theories, laws of error, etc. An appendix covers problems arising from relativity, force, motion, space, and time. A classic in its field. Index. xiii + 565pp. 5⅝ x 8⅜. S372 Paperbound **$2.95**

WHAT IS SCIENCE?, Norman Campbell. This excellent introduction explains scientific method, role of mathematics, types of scientific laws. Contents: 2 aspects of science, science & nature, laws of science, discovery of laws, explanation of laws, measurement & numerical laws, applications of science. 192pp. 5⅜ x 8. S43 Paperbound **$1.25**

THE VALUE OF SCIENCE, Henri Poincaré. Many of the most mature ideas of the "last scientific universalist" covered with charm and vigor for both the beginning student and the advanced worker. Discusses the nature of scientific truth, whether order is innate in the universe or imposed upon it by man, logical thought versus intuition (relating to math, through the works of Weierstrass, Lie, Klein, Riemann), time and space (relativity, psychological time, simultaneity), Hertz's concept of force, interrelationship of mathematical physics to pure math, values within disciplines of Maxwell, Carnot, Mayer, Newton, Lorentz, etc. Index. iii + 147pp. 5⅜ x 8. S469 Paperbound **$1.35**

SCIENCE AND METHOD, Henri Poincaré. Procedure of scientific discovery, methodology, experiment, idea-germination—the intellectual processes by which discoveries come into being. Most significant and most interesting aspects of development, application of ideas. Chapters cover selection of facts, chance, mathematical reasoning, mathematics, and logic; Whitehead, Russell, Cantor; the new mechanics, etc. 288pp. 5⅜ x 8. S222 Paperbound **$1.35**

SCIENCE AND HYPOTHESIS, Henri Poincaré. Creative psychology in science. How such concepts as number, magnitude, space, force, classical mechanics were developed, and how the modern scientist uses them in his thought. Hypothesis in physics, theories of modern physics. Introduction by Sir James Larmor. "Few mathematicians have had the breadth of vision of Poincaré, and none is his superior in the gift of clear exposition," E. T. Bell. Index. 272pp. 5⅜ x 8. S221 Paperbound **$1.35**

PHILOSOPHY AND THE PHYSICISTS, L. S. Stebbing. The philosophical aspects of modern science examined in terms of a lively critical attack on the ideas of Jeans and Eddington. Discusses the task of science, causality, determinism, probability, consciousness, the relation of the world of physics to that of everyday experience. Probes the philosophical significance of the Planck-Bohr concept of discontinuous energy levels, the inferences to be drawn from Heisenberg's Uncertainty Principle, the implications of "becoming" involved in the 2nd law of thermodynamics, and other problems posed by the discarding of Laplacean determinism. 285pp. 5⅜ x 8. T480 Paperbound **$1.65**

EXPERIMENT AND THEORY IN PHYSICS, Max Born. A Nobel laureate examines the nature and value of the counterclaims of experiment and theory in physics. Synthetic versus analytical scientific advances are analyzed in the work of Einstein, Bohr, Heisenberg, Planck, Eddington, Milne, and others by a fellow participant. 44pp. 5⅜ x 8. S308 Paperbound **60¢**

BIBLIOGRAPHIES

GUIDE TO THE LITERATURE OF MATHEMATICS AND PHYSICS, N. G. Parke III. Over 5000 entries included under approximately 120 major subject headings, of selected most important books, monographs, periodicals, articles in English, plus important works in German, French, Italian, Spanish, Russian (many recently available works). Covers every branch of physics, math, related engineering. Includes author, title, edition, publisher, place, date, number of volumes, number of pages. A 40-page introduction on the basic problems of research and study provides useful information on the organization and use of libraries, the psychology of learning, etc. This reference work will save you hours of time. 2nd revised edition. Indices of authors, subjects. 464pp. 5⅜ x 8. S447 Paperbound **$2.49**

THE STUDY OF THE HISTORY OF MATHEMATICS & THE STUDY OF THE HISTORY OF SCIENCE, George Sarton. Scientific method & philosophy in 2 scholarly fields. Defines duty of historian of math., provides especially useful bibliography with best available biographies of modern mathematicians, editions of their collected works, correspondence. Observes combination of history & science, will aid scholar in understanding science today. Bibliography includes best known treatises on historical methods. 200-item critically evaluated bibliography. Index. 10 illustrations. 2 volumes bound as one. 113pp. + 75pp. 5⅜ x 8. T240 Paperbound **$1.25**

MATHEMATICAL PUZZLES

AMUSEMENTS IN MATHEMATICS, Henry Ernest Dudeney. The foremost British originator of mathematical puzzles is always intriguing, witty, and paradoxical in this classic, one of the largest collections of mathematical amusements. More than 430 puzzles, problems, and paradoxes. Mazes and games, problems on number manipulation, unicursal and other route problems, puzzles on measuring, weighing, packing, age, kinship, chessboards, joiners', crossing river, plane figure dissection, and many others. Solutions. More than 450 illustrations. vii + 258pp. 5⅜ x 8. T473 Paperbound **$1.25**

THE CANTERBURY PUZZLES, Henry Ernest Dudeney. Chaucer's pilgrims set one another problems in story form. Also Adventures of the Puzzle Club, the Strange Escape of the King's Jester, the Monks of Riddlewell, the Squire's Christmas Puzzle Party, and others. All puzzles are original, based on dissecting plane figures, arithmetic, algebra, elementary calculus, and other branches of mathematics, and purely logical ingenuity. "The limit of ingenuity and intricacy . . ." The Observer. Over 110 puzzles. Full solutions. 150 illustrations. viii + 225pp. 5⅜ x 8. T474 Paperbound **$1.25**

SYMBOLIC LOGIC and THE GAME OF LOGIC, Lewis Carroll. "Symbolic Logic" is not concerned with modern symbolic logic, but is instead a collection of over 380 problems posed with charm and imagination, using the syllogism, and a fascinating diagrammatic method of drawing conclusions. In "The Game of Logic," Carroll's whimsical imagination devises a logical game played with 2 diagrams and counters (included) to manipulate hundreds of tricky syllogisms. The final section, "Hit or Miss" is a lagniappe of 101 additional puzzles in the delightful Carroll manner. Until this reprint edition, both of these books were rarities costing up to $15 each. Symbolic Logic: Index, xxxi + 199pp. The Game of Logic: 96pp. Two vols. bound as one. 5⅜ x 8. T492 Paperbound **$1.50**

PILLOW PROBLEMS and A TANGLED TALE, Lewis Carroll. One of the rarest of all Carroll's works, "Pillow Problems" contains 72 original math puzzles, all typically ingenious. Particularly fascinating are Carroll's answers which remain exactly as he thought them out, reflecting his actual mental processes. The problems in "A Tangled Tale" are in story form, originally appearing as a monthly magazine serial. Carroll not only gives the solutions, but uses answers sent in by readers to discuss wrong approaches and misleading paths, and grades them for insight. Both of these books were rarities until this edition, "Pillow Problems" costing up to $25, and "A Tangled Tale" $15. Pillow Problems: Preface and introduction by Lewis Carroll. xx + 109pp. A Tangled Tale: 6 illustrations. 152pp. Two vols. bound as one. 5⅜ x 8. T493 Paperbound **$1.50**

DIVERSIONS AND DIGRESSIONS OF LEWIS CARROLL. A major new treasure for Carroll fans! Rare privately published puzzles, mathematical amusements and recreations, games. Includes the fragmentary Part III of "Curiosa Mathematica." Also contains humorous and satirical pieces: "The New Belfry," "The Vision of the Three T's," and much more. New 32-page supplement of rare photographs taken by Carroll. Formerly titled "The Lewis Carroll Picture Book." Edited by S. Collingwood. x + 375pp. 5⅜ x 8. T732 Paperbound **$1.50**

MATHEMATICAL PUZZLES OF SAM LOYD, Vol. I, selected and edited by M. Gardner. Puzzles by the greatest puzzle creator and innovator. Selected from his famous "Cyclopedia of Puzzles," they retain the unique style and historical flavor of the originals. There are posers based on arithmetic, algebra, probability, game theory, route tracing, topology, counter, sliding block, operations research, geometrical dissection. Includes his famous "14-15" puzzle which was a national craze, and his "Horse of a Different Color" which sold millions of copies. 117 of his most ingenious puzzles in all, 120 line drawings and diagrams. Solutions. Selected references. xx + 167pp. 5⅜ x 8. T498 Paperbound **$1.00**

MATHEMATICAL PUZZLES OF SAM LOYD, Vol. II, selected and edited by Martin Gardner. The outstanding second selection from the great American innovator's "Cyclopedia of Puzzles": speed and distance problems, clock problems, plane and solid geometry, calculus problems, etc. Analytical table of contents that groups the puzzles according to the type of mathematics necessary to solve them. 166 puzzles, 150 original line drawings and diagrams. Selected references. xiv + 177pp. 5⅜ x 8. T709 Paperbound **$1.00**

CALIBAN'S PROBLEM BOOK: MATHEMATICAL, INFERENTIAL, AND CRYPTOGRAPHIC PUZZLES, H. Phillips ("Caliban"), S. T. Shovelton, G. S. Marshall. 105 ingenious problems by the greatest living creator of puzzles based on logic and inference. Rigorous, modern, piquant, and reflecting their author's unusual personality, these intermediate and advanced puzzles all involve the ability to reason clearly through complex situations; some call for mathematical knowledge, ranging from algebra to number theory. Solutions. xi + 180pp. 5⅜ x 8. T736 Paperbound **$1.25**

MATHEMATICAL PUZZLES FOR BEGINNERS AND ENTHUSIASTS, G. Mott-Smith. 188 mathematical puzzles to test mental agility. Inference, interpretation, algebra, dissection of plane figures, geometry, properties of numbers, decimation, permutations, probability, all enter these delightful problems. Puzzles like the Odic Force, How to Draw an Ellipse, Spider's Cousin, more than 180 others. Detailed solutions. Appendix with square roots, triangular numbers, primes, etc. 135 illustrations. 2nd revised edition. 248pp. 5⅜ x 8. T198 Paperbound **$1.00**

INGENIOUS MATHEMATICAL PROBLEMS AND METHODS, L. A. Graham. 100 best problems from Graham "Dial," at least ¾ absolutely original in book form, submitted by applied mathematicians and math puzzle fans. Posed in practical terms, utilize number theory, statistics, compass geometry, networks, inversion, in proofs. Accent on heuristics (problem-solving technique) with various methods of solution discussed, compared, for each problem. First publication. Full solutions. 254pp. 5⅜ x 8. T545 Paperbound **$1.45**

101 PUZZLES IN THOUGHT AND LOGIC, C. R. Wylie, Jr. Designed for readers who enjoy the challenge and stimulation of logical puzzles without specialized mathematical or scientific knowledge. These problems are entirely new, and range from relatively easy to brain-teasers that will afford hours of subtle entertainment. It contains detective puzzles, how to find the lying fisherman, how a blind man can identify color by logic, and many more. Easy-to-understand introduction to the logic of puzzle solving and general scientific method. 128pp. 5⅜ x 8. T367 Paperbound **$1.00**

MAZES AND LABYRINTHS: A BOOK OF PUZZLES, W. Shepherd. Mazes, formerly associated with mystery and ritual, are still among the most intriguing of intellectual puzzles. This is a novel and different collection of 50 amusements that embody the principle of the maze: mazes in the classical tradition; 3-dimensional, ribbon, and Möbius-strip mazes; hidden messages; spatial arrangements; etc.—almost all built on amusing story situations. 84 illustrations. Essay on maze psychology. Solutions. xv + 122pp. 5⅜ x 8. T731 Paperbound **$1.00**

MATHEMAGIC, MAGIC PUZZLES, AND GAMES WITH NUMBERS, Royal V. Heath. Over 60 new puzzles and stunts based on properties of numbers. Demonstrates easy techniques for multiplying large numbers mentally, identifying unknown numbers, determining date of any day in any year, dozens of similar useful, entertaining applications of mathematics. Entertainments like The Lost Digit, 3 Acrobats, Psychic Bridge, magic squares, triangles, cubes, circles, other material not easily found elsewhere. Edited by J. S. Meyer. 76 illustrations. 128pp. 5⅜ x 8 T110 Paperbound **$1.00**

MATHEMATICAL RECREATIONS, M. Kraitchik. Some 250 puzzles, problems, demonstrations of recreational mathematics for beginners & advanced mathematicians. Unusual historical problems from Greek, Medieval, Arabic, Hindu sources: modern problems based on "mathematics without numbers," geometry, topology, arithmetic, etc. Pastimes derived from figurative numbers, Mersenne numbers, Fermat numbers; fairy chess, latruncles, reversi, many topics. Full solutions. Excellent for insights into special fields of math. 181 illustrations. 330pp. 5⅜ x 8. T163 Paperbound **$1.75**

PUZZLE QUIZ AND STUNT FUN, Jerome Meyer. 238 high-priority puzzles, stunts, and tricks—mathematical puzzles like The Clever Carpenter, Atom Bomb, Please Help Alice; mysteries and deductions like The Bridge of Sighs, Dog Logic, Secret Code; observation puzzlers like The American Flag, Playing Cards, Telephone Dial; more than 200 others involving magic squares, tongue twisters, puns, anagrams, word design. Answers included. Revised, enlarged edition of FUN-TO-DO. Over 100 illustrations. 238 puzzles, stunts, tricks. 256pp. 5⅜ x 8. T337 Paperbound **$1.00**

THE BOOK OF MODERN PUZZLES, G. L. Kaufman. More than 150 word puzzles, logic puzzles. No warmed-over fare but all new material based on same appeals that make crosswords and deduction puzzles popular, but with different principles, techniques. Two-minute teasers, involved word-labyrinths, design and pattern puzzles, puzzles calling for logic and observation, puzzles testing ability to apply general knowledge to peculiar situations, many others. Answers to all problems. 116 illustrations. 192pp. 5⅜ x 8. T143 Paperbound **$1.00**

NEW WORD PUZZLES, Gerald L. Kaufman. Contains 100 brand new challenging puzzles based on words and their combinations, never published before in any form. Most are new types invented by the author—for beginners or experts. Chess word puzzles, addle letter anagrams, double word squares, double horizontals, alphagram puzzles, dual acrostigrams, linkogram lapwords—plus 8 other brand new types, all with solutions included. 196 figures. 100 brand new puzzles. vi + 122pp. 5⅜ x 8. T344 Paperbound **$1.00**

MATHEMATICAL RECREATIONS

MATHEMATICS, MAGIC AND MYSTERY, Martin Gardner. Card tricks, feats of mental mathematics, stage mind-reading, other "magic" explained as applications of probability, sets, theory of numbers, topology, various branches of mathematics. Creative examination of laws and their applications with scores of new tricks and insights. 115 sections discuss tricks wtih cards, dice, coins; geometrical vanishing tricks, dozens of others. No sleight of hand needed; mathematics guarantees success. 115 illustrations. xii + 174pp. 5⅜ x 8.
T335 Paperbound **$1.00**

MATHEMATICAL EXCURSIONS, Helen A. Merrill. Fun, recreation, insights into elementary problem-solving. A mathematical expert guides you along by-paths not generally travelled in elementary math courses—how to divide by inspection, Russian peasant system of multiplication; memory systems for pi; building odd and even magic squares; dyadic systems; facts about 37; square roots by geometry; Tchebichev's machine; drawing five-sided figures; dozens more. Solutions to more difficult ones. 50 illustrations. 145pp. 5⅜ x 8.
T350 Paperbound **$1.00**

CRYPTOGRAPHY, L. D. Smith. Excellent elementary introduction to enciphering, deciphering secret writing. Explains transposition, substitution ciphers; codes; solutions. Geometrical patterns, route transcription, columnar transposition, other methods. Mixed cipher systems; single-alphabet, polyalphabetical substitution; mechanical devices; Vigenere system, etc. Enciphering Japanese; explanation of Baconian Biliteral cipher; frequency tables. More than 150 problems provide practical application. Bibliography. Index. 164pp. 5⅜ x 8.
T247 Paperbound **$1.00**

CRYPTANALYSIS, Helen F. Gaines. (Formerly ELEMENTARY CRYPTANALYSIS.) A standard elementary and intermediate text for serious students. It does not confine itself to old material, but contains much that is not generally known, except to experts. Concealment, Transposition, Substitution ciphers; Vigenere, Kasiski, Playfair, multafid, dozens of other techniques. Appendix with sequence charts, letter frequencies in English, 5 other languages, English word frequencies. Bibliography. 167 codes. New to this edition: solution to codes. vi + 230pp. 5⅜ x 8. T97 Paperbound **$1.95**

MAGIC SQUARES AND CUBES, W. S. Andrews. Only book-length treatment in English, a thorough non-technical description and analysis. Here are nasik, overlapping, pandiagonal, serrated squares; magic circles, cubes, spheres, rhombuses. Try your hand at 4-dimensional magical figures! Much unusual folklore and tradition included. High school algebra is sufficient. 754 diagrams and illustrations. viii + 419pp. 5⅜ x 8. T658 Paperbound **$1.85**

PAPER FOLDING FOR BEGINNERS, W. D. Murray and F. J. Rigney. A delightful introduction to the varied and entertaining Japanese art of origami (paper folding), with a full crystal-clear text that anticipates every difficulty; over 275 clearly labeled diagrams of all important stages in creation. You get results at each stage, since complex figures are logically developed from simpler ones. 43 different pieces are explained: place mats, drinking cups, bonbon boxes, sailboats, frogs, roosters, etc. 6 photographic plates. 279 diagrams. 95pp. 5⅝ x 8⅜.
T713 Paperbound **$1.00**

CHESS, CHECKERS, GAMES, GO

A TREASURY OF CHESS LORE, edited by Fred Reinfeld. A delightful collection of anecdotes, short stories, aphorisms by and about the masters, poems, accounts of games and tournaments, photographs. Hundreds of humorous, pithy, satirical, wise, and historical episodes, comments, and word portraits. A fascinating "must" for chess players; revealing and perhaps seductive to those who wonder what their friends see in the game. 49 photographs (14 full page plates). 12 diagrams. xi + 306pp. 5⅜ x 8. T458 Paperbound **$1.75**

REINFELD ON THE END GAME IN CHESS, Fred Reinfeld. Analyzes 62 end games by Alekhine, Flohr, Tarrasch, Morphy, Bogolyubov, Capablanca, Vidmar, Rubinstein, Lasker, Reshevsky, other masters. Only first-rate book with extensive coverage of error; of immense aid in pointing out errors you might have made. Centers around transitions from middle play to various types of end play. King & pawn endings, minor piece endings, queen endings, bad bishops, blockage, weak pawns, passed pawns, etc. Formerly titled PRACTICAL END-GAME PLAY. 62 figures. vi + 177pp. 5⅜ x 8. T417 Paperbound **$1.25**

HOW TO FORCE CHECKMATE, Fred Reinfeld. If you have trouble finishing off your opponent, this book is for you. It is a collection of lightning strokes and combinations from actual tournament play. Starting with one-move checkmates and working up to three-move mates, you develop the ability to look ahead, and gain new insights into combinations, complex or deceptive positions, and ways of estimating both your own and your opponent's strengths and weaknesses. 300 diagrams. Solutions to all positions. Formerly entitled CHALLENGE TO CHESS PLAYERS. 111pp. 5⅜ x 8. T439 Paperbound **$1.25**

CHESSBOARD MAGIC! A COLLECTION OF 160 BRILLIANT ENDINGS, compiled, annotated by Irving Chernev. Illustrate not only ingenuity of composition, method of solution, but inherent beauty of solution. Many, by foremost Russian chess authorities, have won first prize in Russian chess magazines; are unavailable in this country. "Marvelous . . . sheer magic," Emanuel Lasker. "An endless feast of delight," Reuben Fine. Introduction. 160 diagrams. Index. 184pp. 5⅜ x 8. T607 Paperbound **$1.00**

LEARN CHESS FROM THE MASTERS, Fred Reinfeld. Improve your chess, rate your improvement, by playing against Marshall, Znosko-Borovsky, Bronstein, Najdorf, others. Formerly titled CHESS BY YOURSELF, this book contains 10 games in which you move against masters, and grade your moves by an easy system. Games selected for interest, clarity, easy principles; illustrate common openings, both classical and modern. Ratings for 114 extra playing situations that might have arisen. Full annotations. 91 diagrams. viii + 144pp. 5⅜ x 8. T362 Paperbound **$1.00**

MORPHY'S GAMES OF CHESS, edited by Philip W. Sergeant. You can put boldness into your game by following the brilliant, forceful moves of the man who has been called the greatest chess player of all time. Here are 300 of Morphy's best games, carefully annotated to reveal Morphy's principles. 54 classics against masters like Anderssen, Harrwitz, Bird, Paulsen, and others. 52 games at odds; 54 blindfold games; plus over 100 others. Unabridged reissue of the latest revised edition. Bibliography. New introduction by Fred Reinfeld. Annotations and introduction by Sergeant. Index. 235 diagrams. x + 352pp. 5⅜ x 8. T386 Paperbound **$1.75**

MODERN IDEAS IN CHESS, R. Réti. Clearest and most readable explanation of major developments in chess styles. Concentrates on the games of the master most closely associated with each major advance of the last hundred years. Seven world champions (Anderssen, Morphy, Steinitz, Lasker, Capablanca, Alekhine, and Euwe) are analyzed by a modern master. 34 diagrams. 192pp. 5⅜ x 8. T638 Paperbound **$1.25**

THE BOOK OF THE NEW YORK INTERNATIONAL CHESS TOURNAMENT, 1924, annotated by A. Alekhine and edited by H. Helms. Long a rare collector's item, this is the book of one of the most brilliant tournaments of all time, during which Capablanca, Dr. Lasker, Alekhine, Reti, and others immeasurably enriched chess theory in a thrilling contest. All 110 games played, with Alekhine's unusually penetrating notes. 15 photographs. xi + 271pp. 5⅜ x 8. T752 Paperboard **$1.85**

KERES' BEST GAMES OF CHESS, selected, annotated by F. Reinfeld. 90 best games, 1931-1948, by one of boldest, most exciting players of modern chess. Games against Alekhine, Bogolyubov, Capablanca, Euwe, Fine, Reshevsky, other masters, show his treatments of openings such as Giuoco Piano, Alekhine Defense, Queen's Gambit Declined; attacks, sacrifices, alternative methods. Preface by Keres gives personal glimpses, evaluations of rivals. 110 diagrams. 272pp. 5⅜ x 8. T593 Paperbound **$1.35**

THE DEVELOPMENT OF A CHESS GENIUS: 100 INSTRUCTIVE GAMES OF ALEKHINE, by Fred Reinfeld. Games from vital formative years 1905-1914, most of them never before in book form, show a future great master being shaped by experience and challenge in matches against Bernstein, Bogolyubov, Capablanca, Marshall, Rubinstein, Tarrasch, others. Interesting as chess biography, instructive as a master's increasingly adept responses to problems of every player. Annotated by F. Reinfeld. "One of America's most significant contributions," Chess Life. Formerly "The Unknown Alekhine." Introduction. Indexes of players, openings. 204 illustrations. 242pp. 5⅜ x 8. T551 Paperbound **$1.35**

RESHEVSKY'S BEST GAMES OF CHESS, Samuel Reshevsky. One time 4-year old chess genius, 5-time winner U. S. Chess Championship, selects, annotates 110 of his best games, illustrating theories, favorite methods of play against Capablanca, Alekhine, Bogolyubov, Kashdan, Vidmar, Botvinnik, others. Clear, non-technical style. Personal impressions of opponents, autobiographical material, tournament match record. Formerly, "Reshevsky on Chess." 309 diagrams, 2 photos. 288pp. 5⅜ x 8. T606 Paperbound **$1.25**

GO AND GO-MOKU: THE ORIENTAL BOARD GAMES, Edward Lasker. Best introduction to Go and its easier sister-game, Go-Moku—games new to Western world, but ancient in China, Japan. Extensively revised work by famed chess master Lasker, Go-player for over 50 years, stresses theory rather than brute memory, presents step-by-step explanation of strategy, gives examples of world championship matches, in game which has replaced chess as favorite of many physicists, mathematicians. 72 diagrams. xix + 215 pp. 5⅜ x 8.
T613 Paperbound **$1.45**

FICTION

FLATLAND, E. A. Abbott. A science-fiction classic of life in a 2-dimensional world that is also a first-rate introduction to such aspects of modern science as relativity and hyperspace. Political, moral, satirical, and humorous overtones have made FLATLAND fascinating reading for thousands. 7th edition. New introduction by Banesh Hoffmann. 16 illustrations. 128pp. 5⅜ x 8.
T1 Paperbound **$1.00**

THE WONDERFUL WIZARD OF OZ, L. F. Baum. Only edition in print with all the original W. W. Denslow illustrations in full color—as much a part of "The Wizard" as Tenniel's drawings are of "Alice in Wonderland." "The Wizard" is still America's best-loved fairy tale, in which, as the author expresses it, "The wonderment and joy are retained and the heartaches and nightmares left out." Now today's young readers can enjoy every word and wonderful picture of the original book. New introduction by Martin Gardner. A Baum bibliography. 23 full-page color plates. viii + 268pp. 5⅜ x 8. T691 Paperbound **$1.45**

THE MARVELOUS LAND OF OZ, L. F. Baum. This is the equally enchanting sequel to the "Wizard," continuing the adventures of the Scarecrow and the Tin Woodman. The hero this time is a little boy named Tip, and all the delightful Oz magic is still present. This is the book with the Animated Saw-horse, the Woggle-Bug, and Jack Pumpkinhead. All the original John R. Neill illustrations, 16 in full color. 287pp. 5⅜ x 8. T692 Paperbound **$1.45**

FIVE GREAT DOG NOVELS, edited by Blanche Cirker. The complete original texts of five classic dog novels that have delighted and thrilled millions of children and adults throughout the world with stories of loyalty, adventure, and courage. Full texts of Jack London's "The Call of the Wild"; John Brown's "Rab and His Friends"; Alfred Ollivant's "Bob, Son of Battle"; Marshall Saunders' "Beautiful Joe"; and Ouida's "A Dog of Flanders." 21 illustrations from the original editions. 495pp. 5⅜ x 8. T777 Paperbound **$1.50**

3 ADVENTURE NOVELS by H. Rider Haggard. Complete texts of "She," "King Solomon's Mines," "Allan Quatermain." Qualities of discovery; desire for immortality; search for primitive, for what is unadorned by civilization, have kept these novels of African adventure exciting, alive to readers from R. L. Stevenson to George Orwell. 636pp. 5⅜ x 8.
T584 Paperbound **$2.00**

The Space Novels of Jules Verne

TO THE SUN? and OFF ON A COMET!, Jules Verne. Complete texts of two of the most imaginative flights into fancy in world literature display the high adventure that have kept Verne's novels read for nearly a century. Only unabridged edition of the best translation, by Edward Roth. Large, easily readable type. 50 illustrations selected from first editions. 462pp. 5⅜ x 8.
T634 Paperbound **$1.75**

FROM THE EARTH TO THE MOON and ALL AROUND THE MOON, Jules Verne. Complete editions of two of Verne's most successful novels, in finest Edward Roth translations, now available after many years out of print. Verne's visions of submarines, airplanes, television, rockets, interplanetary travel; of scientific and not-so-scientific beliefs; of peculiarities of Americans; all delight and engross us today as much as when they first appeared. Large, easily readable type. 42 illus. from first French edition. 476pp. 5⅜ x 8.
T633 Paperbound **$1.75**

THE CASTING AWAY OF MRS. LECKS AND MRS. ALESHINE, F. R. Stockton. A charming light novel by Frank Stockton, one of America's finest humorists (and author of "The Lady, or the Tiger?"). This book has made millions of Americans laugh at the reflection of themselves in two middle-aged American women involved in some of the strangest adventures on record. You will laugh, too, as they endure shipwreck, desert island, and blizzard with maddening tranquility. Also contains complete text of "The Dusantes," sequel to "The Casting Away." 49 original illustrations by F. D. Steele. vii + 142pp. 5⅜ x 8. T743 Paperbound **$1.00**

GESTA ROMANORUM, trans. by Charles Swan, ed. by Wynnard Hooper. 181 tales of Greeks, Romans, Britons, Biblical characters, comprise one of greatest medieval story collections, source plots for writers including Shakespeare, Chaucer, Gower, etc. Imaginative tales of wars, incest, thwarted love, magic, fantasy, allegory, humor, tell about kings, prostitutes, philosophers, fair damsels, knights, Noah, pirates, all walks and stations of life. Introduction. Notes. 500pp. 5⅜ x 8. T535 Paperbound **$1.85**

THREE PROPHETIC NOVELS BY H. G. WELLS, edited by E. F. Bleiler. Complete texts of "When the Sleeper Wakes" (1st book printing in 50 years), "A Story of the Days to Come," "The Time Machine" (1st complete printing in book form). Exciting adventures in the future are as enjoyable today as 50 years ago when first printed. Predict TV, movies, intercontinental airplanes, prefabricated houses, air-conditioned cities, etc. First important author to foresee problems of mind control, technological dictatorships. "Absolute best of imaginative fiction," N. Y. Times. Introduction. 335pp. 5⅜ x 8. T605 Paperbound **$1.45**

SEVEN SCIENCE FICTION NOVELS, H. G. Wells. Full unabridged texts of 7 science-fiction novels of the master. Ranging from biology, physics, chemistry, astronomy to sociology and other studies, Mr. Wells extrapolates whole worlds of strange and intriguing character. "One will have to go far to match this for entertainment, excitement, and sheer pleasure . . . ," NEW YORK TIMES. Contents: The Time Machine, The Island of Dr. Moreau, First Men in the Moon, The Invisible Man, The War of the Worlds, The Food of the Gods, In the Days of the Comet. 1015pp. 5⅜ x 8. T264 Clothbound **$3.95**

28 SCIENCE FICTION STORIES OF H. G. WELLS. Two full unabridged novels, MEN LIKE GODS and STAR BEGOTTEN, plus 26 short stories by the master science-fiction writer of all time. Stories of space, time, invention, exploration, future adventure—an indispensable part of the library of everyone interested in science and adventure. PARTIAL CONTENTS: Men Like Gods, The Country of the Blind, In the Abyss, The Crystal Egg, The Man Who Could Work Miracles, A Story of the Days to Come, The Valley of Spiders, and 21 more! 928pp. 5⅜ x 8. T265 Clothbound **$3.95**

DAVID HARUM, E. N. Westcott. This novel of one of the most lovable, humorous characters in American literature is a prime example of regional humor. It continues to delight people who like their humor dry, their characters quaint, and their plots ingenuous. First book edition to contain complete novel plus chapter found after author's death. Illustrations from first illustrated edition. 192pp. 5⅜ x 8. T580 Paperbound **$1.15**

HUMOR

THE WIT AND HUMOR OF OSCAR WILDE, ed. by Alvin Redman. Wilde at his most brilliant, in 1000 epigrams exposing weaknesses and hypocrisies of "civilized" society. Divided into 49 categories—sin, wealth, women, America, etc.—to aid writers, speakers. Includes excerpts from his trials, books, plays, criticism. Formerly "The Epigrams of Oscar Wilde." Introduction by Vyvyan Holland, Wilde's only living son. Introductory essay by editor. 260pp. 5⅜ x 8. T602 Paperbound **$1.00**

A NONSENSE ANTHOLOGY, collected by **Carolyn Wells.** 245 of the best nonsense verses ever written, including nonsense puns, absurd arguments, mock epics and sagas, nonsense ballads, odes, "sick" verses, dog-Latin verses, French nonsense verses, songs. By Edward Lear, Lewis Carroll, Gelett Burgess, W. S. Gilbert, Hilaire Belloc, Peter Newell, Oliver Herford, etc., 83 writers in all plus over four score anonymous nonsense verses. A special section of limericks, plus famous nonsense such as Carroll's "Jabberwocky" and Lear's "The Jumblies" and much excellent verse virtually impossible to locate elsewhere. For 50 years considered the best anthology available. Index of first lines specially prepared for this edition. Introduction by Carolyn Wells. 3 indexes: Title, Author, First lines. xxxiii + 279pp. 5⅜ x 8. T499 Paperbound **$1.25**

THE BAD CHILD'S BOOK OF BEASTS, MORE BEASTS FOR WORSE CHILDREN, and A MORAL ALPHABET, H. Belloc. Hardly an anthology of humorous verse has appeared in the last 50 years without at least a couple of these famous nonsense verses. But one must see the entire volumes—with all the delightful original illustrations by Sir Basil Blackwood—to appreciate fully Belloc's charming and witty verses that play so subacidly on the platitudes of life and morals that beset his day—and ours. A great humor classic. Three books in one. Total of 157pp. 5⅜ x 8. T749 Paperbound **$1.00**

THE DEVIL'S DICTIONARY, Ambrose Bierce. Sardonic and irreverent barbs puncturing the pomposities and absurdities of American politics, business, religion, literature, and arts, by the country's greatest satirist in the classic tradition. Epigrammatic as Shaw, piercing as Swift, American as Mark Twain, Will Rogers, and Fred Allen. Bierce will always remain the favorite of a small coterie of enthusiasts, and of writers and speakers whom he supplies with "some of the most gorgeous witticisms of the English language." (H. L. Mencken) Over 1000 entries in alphabetical order. 144pp. 5⅜ x 8. T487 Paperbound **$1.00**

THE PURPLE COW AND OTHER NONSENSE, Gelett Burgess. The best of Burgess's early nonsense, selected from the first edition of the "Burgess Nonsense Book." Contains many of his most unusual and highly original pieces: 37 nonsense quatrains, the Poems of Patagonia, Alphabet of Famous Goops, and the other hilarious (and rare) adult nonsense that places him in the forefront of American humorists. All pieces are accompanied by the original Burgess illustrations. 123 illustrations. xiii + 113pp. 5⅜ x 8.
T772 Paperbound **$1.00**

THE HUMOROUS VERSE OF LEWIS CARROLL. Almost every poem Carroll ever wrote, the largest collection ever published, including much never published elsewhere: 150 parodies, burlesques, riddles, ballads, acrostics, etc., with 130 original illustrations by Tenniel, Carroll, and others. "Addicts will be grateful . . . there is nothing for the faithful to do but sit down and fall to the banquet," N. Y. Times. Index to first lines. xiv + 446pp. 5 x 8.
T654 Paperbound **$1.85**

DIVERSIONS AND DIGRESSIONS OF LEWIS CARROLL. A major new treasure for Carroll fans! Rare privately published humor, fantasy, puzzles, and games by Carroll at his whimsical best, with a new vein of frank satire. Includes many new mathematical amusements and recreations, among them the fragmentary Part III of "Curiosa Mathematica." Contains "The Rectory Umbrella," "The New Belfry," "The Vision of the Three T's," and much more. New 32-page supplement of rare photographs taken by Carroll. x + 375pp. 5⅜ x 8.
T732 Paperbound **$1.50**

THE COMPLETE NONSENSE OF EDWARD LEAR. This is the only complete edition of this master of gentle madness available at a popular price. A BOOK OF NONSENSE, NONSENSE SONGS, MORE NONSENSE SONGS AND STORIES in their entirety with all the old favorites that have delighted children and adults for years. The Dong With A Luminous Nose, The Jumblies, The Owl and the Pussycat, and hundreds of other bits of wonderful nonsense. 214 limericks, 3 sets of Nonsense Botany, 5 Nonsense Alphabets. 546 drawings by Lear himself, and much more. 320pp. 5⅜ x 8.
T167 Paperbound **$1.00**

PECK'S BAD BOY AND HIS PA, George W. Peck. The complete edition, containing both volumes, one of the most widely read of all American humor books. The endless ingenious pranks played by bad boy "Hennery" on his pa and the grocery man, the outraged pomposity of Pa, the perpetual ridiculing of middle class institutions, are as entertaining today as they were in 1883. No pale sophistications or subtleties, but rather humor vigorous, raw, earthy, imaginative, and, as folk humor often is, sadistic. This peculiarly fascinating book is also valuable to historians and students of American culture as a portrait of an age. 100 original illustrations by True Williams. Introduction by E. F. Bleiler. 347pp. 5⅜ x 8.
T497 Paperbound **$1.35**

FABLES IN SLANG & MORE FABLES IN SLANG, George Ade. 2 complete books of major American humorist in pungent colloquial tradition of Twain, Billings. 1st reprinting in over 30 years includes "The Two Mandolin Players and the Willing Performer," "The Base Ball Fan Who Took the Only Known Cure," "The Slim Girl Who Tried to Keep a Date that was Never Made," 42 other tales of eccentric, perverse, but always funny characters. "Touch of genius," H. L. Mencken. New introduction by E. F. Bleiler. 86 illus. 203pp. 5⅜ x 8.
T533 Paperbound **$1.00**

SINGULAR TRAVELS, CAMPAIGNS, AND ADVENTURES OF BARON MUNCHAUSEN, R. E. Raspe, with 90 illustrations by Gustave Doré. The first edition in over 150 years to reestablish the deeds of the Prince of Liars exactly as Raspe first recorded them in 1785—the genuine Baron Munchausen, one of the most popular personalities in English literature. Included also are the best of the many sequels, written by other hands. Introduction on Raspe by J. Carswell. Bibliography of early editions. xliv + 192pp. 5⅜ x 8. T698 Paperbound **$1.00**

HOW TO TELL THE BIRDS FROM THE FLOWERS, R. W. Wood. How not to confuse a carrot with a parrot, a grape with an ape, a puffin with nuffin. Delightful drawings, clever puns, absurd little poems point out farfetched resemblances in nature. The author was a leading physicist. Introduction by Margaret Wood White. 106 illus. 60pp. 5⅜ x 8.
T523 Paperbound **75¢**

MATHEMATICS, ELEMENTARY TO INTERMEDIATE

HOW TO CALCULATE QUICKLY, Henry Sticker. This handy volume offers a tried and true method for helping you in the basic mathematics of daily life—addition, subtraction, multiplication, division, fractions, etc. It is designed to awaken your "number sense" or the ability to see relationships between numbers as whole quantities. It is not a collection of tricks working only on special numbers, but a serious course of over 9,000 problems and their solutions, teaching special techniques not taught in schools: left-to-right multiplication, new fast ways of division, etc. 5 or 10 minutes daily use will double or triple your calculation speed. Excellent for the scientific worker who is at home in higher math, but is not satisfied with his speed and accuracy in lower mathematics. 256pp. 5 x 7¼. T295 Paperbound **$1.00**

TEACH YOURSELF books. For adult self-study, for refresher and supplementary study.

The most effective series of home study mathematics books on the market! With absolutely no outside help, they will teach you as much as any similar college or high-school course, or will helpfully supplement any such course. Each step leads directly to the next, each question is anticipated. Numerous lucid examples and carefully-wrought practice problems illustrate meanings. Not skimpy outlines, not surveys, not usual classroom texts, these 204- to 380-page books are packed with the finest instruction you'll find anywhere for adult self-study.

TEACH YOURSELF ALGEBRA, P. Abbott. Formulas, coordinates, factors, graphs of quadratic functions, quadratic equations, logarithms, ratio, irrational numbers, arithmetical, geometrical series, much more. 1241 problems, solutions. Tables. 52 illus. 307pp. 6⅞ x 4¼.
Clothbound **$2.00**

TEACH YOURSELF GEOMETRY, P. Abbott. Solids, lines, points, surfaces, angle measurement, triangles, theorem of Pythagoras, polygons, loci, the circle, tangents, symmetry, solid geometry, prisms, pyramids, solids of revolution, etc. 343 problems, solutions. 268 illus. 334pp. 6⅞ x 4¼. Clothbound **$2.00**

TEACH YOURSELF TRIGONOMETRY, P. Abbott. Geometrical foundations, indices, logarithms, trigonometrical ratios, relations between sides, angles of triangle, circular measure, trig. ratios of angles of any magnitude, much more. Requires elementary algebra, geometry. 465 problems, solutions. Tables. 102 illus. 204pp. 6⅞ x 4¼. Clothbound **$2.00**

TEACH YOURSELF THE CALCULUS, P. Abbott. Variations in functions, differentiation, solids of revolution, series, elementary differential equations, areas by integral calculus, much more. Requires algebra, trigonometry. 970 problems, solutions. Tables. 89 illus. 380pp. 6⅞ x 4¼.
Clothbound **$2.00**

TEACH YOURSELF THE SLIDE RULE, B. Snodgrass. Fractions, decimals, A-D scales, log-log scales, trigonometrical scales, indices, logarithms. Commercial, precision, electrical, dualistic, Brighton rules. 80 problems, solutions. 10 illus. 207pp. 6⅞ x 4¼. Clothbound **$2.00**

See also: **TEACH YOURSELF ELECTRICITY, C. W. Wilman; TEACH YOURSELF HEAT ENGINES, E. De Ville; TEACH YOURSELF MECHANICS, P. Abbott.**

* * *

HOW DO YOU USE A SLIDE RULE? by A. A. Merrill. Not a manual for mathematicians and engineers, but a lucid step-by-step explanation that presents the fundamental rules clearly enough to be understood by anyone who could benefit by the use of a slide rule in his work or business. This work concentrates on the 2 most important operations: multiplication and division. 10 easy lessons, each with a clear drawing, will save you countless hours in your banking, business, statistical, and other work. First publication. Index. 2 Appendixes. 10 illustrations. 78 problems, all with answers. vi + 36pp. 6⅛ x 9¼. T62 Paperbound **60¢**

THEORY OF OPERATION OF THE SLIDE RULE, J. P. Ellis. Not a skimpy "instruction manual", but an exhaustive treatment that will save you uncounted hours throughout your career. Supplies full understanding of every scale on the Log Log Duplex Decitrig type of slide rule. Shows the most time-saving methods, and provides practice useful in the widest variety of actual engineering situations. Each operation introduced in terms of underlying logarithmic theory. Summary of prerequisite math. First publication. Index. 198 figures. Over 450 problems with answers. Bibliography. 12 Appendices. ix + 289pp. 5⅜ x 8.
S727 Paperbound **$1.50**

ARITHMETICAL EXCURSIONS: AN ENRICHMENT OF ELEMENTARY MATHEMATICS, H. Bowers and J. Bowers. For students who want unusual methods of arithmetic never taught in school; for adults who want to increase their number sense. Little known facts about the most simple numbers, arithmetical entertainments and puzzles, figurate numbers, number chains, mysteries and folklore of numbers, the "Hin-dog-abic" number system, etc. First publication. Index. 529 numbered problems and diversions, all with answers. Bibliography. 50 figures. xiv + 320pp. 5⅜ x 8. T770 Paperbound **$1.65**

APPLIED MATHEMATICS FOR RADIO AND COMMUNICATIONS ENGINEERS, C. E. Smith. No extraneous material here!—only the theories, equations, and operations essential and immediately useful for radio work. Can be used as refresher, as handbook of applications and tables, or as full home-study course. Ranges from simplest arithmetic through calculus, series, and wave forms, hyperbolic trigonometry, simultaneous equations in mesh circuits, etc. Supplies applications right along with each math topic discussed. 22 useful tables of functions, formulas, logs, etc. Index. 166 exercises, 140 examples, all with answers. 95 diagrams. Bibliography. x + 336pp. 5⅜ x 8. S141 Paperbound **$1.75**

FAMOUS PROBLEMS OF ELEMENTARY GEOMETRY, Felix Klein. Expanded version of the 1894 Easter lectures at Göttingen. 3 problems of classical geometry, in an excellent mathematical treatment by a famous mathematician: squaring the circle, trisecting angle, doubling cube. Considered with full modern implications: transcendental numbers, pi, etc. Notes by R. Archibald. 16 figures. xi + 92pp. 5⅜ x 8. T348 Clothbound **$1.50**
T298 Paperbound **$1.00**

* * *

ELEMENTARY MATHEMATICS FROM AN ADVANCED STANDPOINT, Felix Klein.

This classic text is an outgrowth of Klein's famous integration and survey course at Göttingen. Using one field of mathematics to interpret, adjust, illuminate another, it covers basic topics in each area, illustrating its discussion with extensive analysis. It is especially valuable in considering areas of modern mathematics. "Makes the reader feel the inspiration of . . . a great mathematician, inspiring teacher . . . with deep insight into the foundations and interrelations," BULLETIN, AMERICAN MATHEMATICAL SOCIETY.

Vol. 1. ARITHMETIC, ALGEBRA, ANALYSIS. Introducing the concept of function immediately, it enlivens abstract discussion with graphical and geometrically perceptual methods. Partial contents: natural numbers, extension of the notion of number, special properties, complex numbers. Real equations with real unknowns, complex quantities. Logarithmic, exponential functions, goniometric functions, infinitesimal calculus. Transcendence of e and pi, theory of assemblages. Index. 125 figures. ix + 274pp . 5⅜ x 8. S150 Paperbound **$1.75**

Vol. 2. GEOMETRY. A comprehensive view which accompanies the space perception inherent in geometry with analytic formulas which facilitate precise formulation. Partial contents: Simplest geometric manifolds: line segment, Grassmann determinant principles, classification of configurations of space, derivative manifolds. Geometric transformations: affine transformations, projective, higher point transformations, theory of the imaginary. Systematic discussion of geometry and its foundations. Indexes. 141 illustrations. ix + 214pp. 5⅜ x 8.
S151 Paperbound **$1.75**

* * *

COORDINATE GEOMETRY, L. P. Eisenhart. Thorough, unified introduction. Unusual for advancing in dimension within each topic (treats together circle, sphere; polar coordinates, 3-dimensional coordinate systems; conic sections, quadric surfaces), affording exceptional insight into subject. Extensive use made of determinants, though no previous knowledge of them is assumed. Algebraic equations of 1st degree, 2 and 3 unknowns, carried further than usual in algebra courses. Over 500 exercises. Introduction. Appendix. Index. Bibliography. 43 illustrations. 310pp. 5⅜ x 8. S600 Paperbound **$1.65**

MONOGRAPHS ON TOPICS OF MODERN MATHEMATICS, edited by **J. W. A. Young.** Advanced mathematics for persons who haven't gone beyond or have forgotten high school algebra. 9 monographs on foundation of geometry, modern pure geometry, non-Euclidean geometry, fundamental propositions of algebra, algebraic equations, functions, calculus, theory of numbers, etc. Each monograph gives proofs of important results, and descriptions of leading methods, to provide wide coverage. New introduction by Prof. M. Kline, N. Y. University. 100 diagrams. xvi + 416pp. 6⅛ x 9¼. S289 Paperbound **$2.00**

MATHEMATICS, INTERMEDIATE TO ADVANCED

Geometry

THE FOUNDATIONS OF EUCLIDEAN GEOMETRY, H. G. Forder. The first rigorous account of Euclidean geometry, establishing propositions without recourse to empiricism, and without multiplying hypotheses. Corrects many traditional weaknesses of Euclidean proofs, and investigates the problems imposed on the axiom system by the discoveries of Bolya and Lobatchefsky. Some topics discussed are Classes and Relations; Axioms for Magnitudes; Congruence and Similarity; Algebra of Points; Hessenberg's Theorem; Continuity; Existence of Parallels; Reflections; Rotations; Isometries; etc. Invaluable for the light it throws on foundations of math. Lists: Axioms employed, Symbols, Constructions. 295pp. 5⅜ x 8.
S481 Paperbound **$2.00**

ADVANCED EUCLIDEAN GEOMETRY, R. A. Johnson. For years the standard textbook on advanced Euclidean geometry, requires only high school geometry and trigonometry. Explores in unusual detail and gives proofs of hundreds of relatively recent theorems and corollaries, many formerly available only in widely scattered journals. Covers tangent circles, the theorem of Miquel, symmedian point, pedal triangles and circles, the Brocard configuration, and much more. Formerly "Modern Geometry." Index. 107 diagrams. xiii + 319pp. 5⅜ x 8.
S669 Paperbound **$1.65**

NON-EUCLIDEAN GEOMETRY, Roberto Bonola. The standard coverage of non-Euclidean geometry. It examines from both a historical and mathematical point of view the geometries which have arisen from a study of Euclid's 5th postulate upon parallel lines. Also included are complete texts, translated, of Bolyai's THEORY OF ABSOLUTE SPACE, Lobachevsky's THEORY OF PARALLELS. 180 diagrams. 431pp. 5⅜ x 8. S27 Paperbound **$1.95**

ELEMENTS OF NON-EUCLIDEAN GEOMETRY, D. M. Y. Sommerville. Unique in proceeding step-by-step, in the manner of traditional geometry. Enables the student with only a good knowledge of high school algebra and geometry to grasp elementary hyperbolic, elliptic, analytic non-Euclidean geometries; space curvature and its philosophical implications; theory of radical axes; homothetic centres and systems of circles; parataxy and parallelism; absolute measure; Gauss' proof of the defect area theorem; geodesic representation; much more, all with exceptional clarity. 126 problems at chapter endings provide progressive practice and familiarity. 133 figures. Index. xvi + 274pp. 5⅜ x 8. S460 Paperbound **$1.50**

HIGHER GEOMETRY: AN INTRODUCTION TO ADVANCED METHODS IN ANALYTIC GEOMETRY, F. S. Woods. Exceptionally thorough study of concepts and methods of advanced algebraic geometry (as distinguished from differential geometry). Exhaustive treatment of 1-, 2-, 3-, and 4-dimensional coordinate systems, leading to n-dimensional geometry in an abstract sense. Covers projectivity, tetracyclical coordinates, contact transformation, pentaspherical coordinates, much more. Based on M.I.T. lectures, requires sound preparation in analytic geometry and some knowledge of determinants. Index. Over 350 exercises. References. 60 figures. x + 423pp. 5⅜ x 8. S737 Paperbound **$2.00**

ELEMENTS OF PROJECTIVE GEOMETRY, L. Cremona. Outstanding complete treatment of projective geometry by one of the foremost 19th century geometers. Detailed proofs of all fundamental principles, stress placed on the constructive aspects. Covers homology, law of duality, anharmonic ratios, theorems of Pascal and Brianchon, foci, polar reciprocal figures, etc. Only ordinary geometry necessary to understand this honored classic. Index. Over 150 fully worked out examples and problems. 252 diagrams. xx + 302pp. 5⅜ x 8. S668 Paperbound **$1.75**

A TREATISE ON THE DIFFERENTIAL GEOMETRY OF CURVES AND SURFACES, L. P. Eisenhart. Introductory treatise especially for the graduate student, for years a highly successful textbook. More detailed and concrete in approach than most more recent books. Covers space curves, osculating planes, moving axes, Gauss' method, the moving trihedral, geodesics, conformal representation, etc. Last section deals with deformation of surfaces, rectilinear congruences, cyclic systems, etc. Index. 683 problems. 30 diagrams. xii + 474pp. 5⅜ x 8. S667 Paperbound **$2.75**

A TREATISE ON ALGEBRAIC PLANE CURVES, J. L. Coolidge. Unabridged reprinting of one of few full coverages in English, offering detailed introduction to theory of algebraic plane curves and their relations to geometry and analysis. Treats topological properties, Riemann-Roch theorem, all aspects of wide variety of curves including real, covariant, polar, containing series of a given sort, elliptic, polygonal, rational, the pencil, two parameter nets, etc. This volume will enable the reader to appreciate the symbolic notation of Aronhold and Clebsch. Bibliography. Index. 17 illustrations. xxiv + 513pp. 5⅜ x 8. S543 Paperbound **$2.45**

AN INTRODUCTION TO THE GEOMETRY OF N DIMENSIONS, D. M. Y. Sommerville. An introduction presupposing no prior knowledge of the field, the only book in English devoted exclusively to higher dimensional geometry. Discusses fundamental ideas of incidence, parallelism, perpendicularity, angles between linear space; enumerative geometry; analytical geometry from projective and metric points of view; polytopes; elementary ideas in analysis situs; content of hyper-spacial figures. Bibliography. Index. 60 diagrams. 196pp. 5⅜ x 8. S494 Paperbound **$1.50**

GEOMETRY OF FOUR DIMENSIONS, H. P. Manning. Unique in English as a clear, concise introduction. Treatment is synthetic, and mostly Euclidean, although in hyperplanes and hyperspheres at infinity, non-Euclidean geometry is used. Historical introduction. Foundations of 4-dimensional geometry. Perpendicularity, simple angles. Angles of planes, higher order. Symmetry, order, motion; hyperpyramids, hypercones, hyperspheres; figures with parallel elements; volume, hypervolume in space; regular polyhedroids. Glossary. 78 figures. ix + 348pp. 5⅜ x 8. S182 Paperbound **$1.95**

ELEMENTARY CONCEPTS OF TOPOLOGY, P. Alexandroff. First English translation of the famous brief introduction to topology for the beginner or for the mathematician not undertaking extensive study. This unusually useful intuitive approach deals primarily with the concepts of complex, cycle, and homology, and is wholly consistent with current investigations. Ranges from basic concepts of set-theoretic topology to the concept of Betti groups. "Glowing example of harmony between intuition and thought," David Hilbert. Translated by A. E. Farley. Introduction by D. Hilbert. Index. 25 figures. 73pp. 5⅜ x 8. S747 Paperbound **$1.00**

THE WORKS OF ARCHIMEDES, edited by **T. L. Heath.** All the known works of the great Greek mathematician are contained in this one volume, including the recently discovered Method of Archimedes. Contains: On Sphere & Cylinder, Measurement of a Circle, Spirals, Conoids, Spheroids, etc. This is the definitive edition of the greatest mathematical intellect of the ancient world. 186-page study by Heath discusses Archimedes and the history of Greek mathematics. Bibliography. 563pp. 5⅜ x 8. S9 Paperbound **$2.00**

THE THIRTEEN BOOKS OF EUCLID'S ELEMENTS, edited by **Sir Thomas Heath.** Definitive edition of one of the very greatest classics of Western world. Complete English translation of Heiberg text, together with spurious Book XIV. Detailed 150-page introduction discussing aspects of Greek and Medieval mathematics. Euclid, texts, commentators, etc. Paralleling the text is an elaborate critical apparatus analyzing each definition, proposition, postulate, covering textual matters, mathematical analysis, commentators of all times, refutations, supports, extrapolations, etc. This is the FULL EUCLID. Unabridged reproduction of Cambridge U. 2nd edition. 3 volumes. Total of 995 figures, 1426pp. 5⅜ x 8.
S88,89,90, 3 volume set, paperbound **$6.00**

THE GEOMETRY OF RENE DESCARTES. With this book Descartes founded analytical geometry. Excellent Smith-Latham translation, plus original French text with Déscartes' own diagrams. Contains Problems the Construction of Which Requires Only Straight Lines and Circles; On the Nature of Curved Lines; On the Construction of Solid or Supersolid Problems. Notes. Diagrams. 258pp. 5⅜ x 8. S68 Paperbound **$1.50**

See also: **FOUNDATIONS OF GEOMETRY, B. Russell; THE PHILOSOPHY OF SPACE AND TIME, H. Reichenbach; FAMOUS PROBLEMS OF ELEMENTARY GEOMETRY, F. Klein; MONOGRAPHS ON TOPICS OF MODERN MATHEMATICS, ed. by J. W. Young.**

Calculus and function theory, Fourier theory, real and complex functions, determinants

A COLLECTION OF MODERN MATHEMATICAL CLASSICS, edited by R. Bellman. 13 classic papers, complete in their original languages, by Hermite, Hardy and Littlewood, Tchebychef, Fejér, Fredholm, Fuchs, Hurwitz, Weyl, van der Pol, Birkhoff, Kellogg, von Neumann, and Hilbert. Each of these papers, collected here for the first time, triggered a burst of mathematical activity, providing useful new generalizations or stimulating fresh investigations. Topics discussed include classical analysis, periodic and almost periodic functions, analysis and number theory, integral equations, theory of approximation, non-linear differential equations, and functional analysis. Brief introductions and bibliographies to each paper. xii + 292pp. 6 x 9.
S730 Paperbound **$2.00**

MATHEMATICS OF MODERN ENGINEERING, E. G. Keller and R. E. Doherty. Written for the Advanced Course in Engineering of the General Electric Corporation, deals with the engineering use of determinants, tensors, the Heaviside operational calculus, dyadics, the calculus of variations, etc. Presents underlying principles fully, but purpose is to teach engineers to deal with modern engineering problems, and emphasis is on the perennial engineering attack of set-up and solve. Indexes. Over 185 figures and tables. Hundreds of exercises, problems, and worked-out examples. References. Two volume set. Total of xxxiii + 623pp. 5⅜ x 8.
S734 Vol I Paperbound **$1.65**
S735 Vol II Paperbound **$1.65**
The set **$3.30**

MATHEMATICAL METHODS FOR SCIENTISTS AND ENGINEERS, L. P. Smith. For scientists and engineers, as well as advanced math students. Full investigation of methods and practical description of conditions under which each should be used. Elements of real functions, differential and integral calculus, space geometry, theory of residues, vector and tensor analysis, series of Bessel functions, etc. Each method illustrated by completely-worked-out examples, mostly from scientific literature. 368 graded unsolved problems. 100 diagrams. x + 453pp. 5⅝ x 8⅜. S220 Paperbound **$2.00**

THEORY OF FUNCTIONS AS APPLIED TO ENGINEERING PROBLEMS, edited by R. Rothe, F. Ollendorff, and K. Pohlhausen. A series of lectures given at the Berlin Institute of Technology that shows the specific applications of function theory in electrical and allied fields of engineering. Six lectures provide the elements of function theory in a simple and practical form, covering complex quantities and variables, integration in the complex plane, residue theorems, etc. Then 5 lectures show the exact uses of this powerful mathematical tool, with full discussions of problem methods. Index. Bibliography. 108 figures. x + 189pp. 5⅜ x 8.
S733 Paperbound **$1.35**

ADVANCED CALCULUS, E. B. Wilson. An unabridged reprinting of the work which continues to be recognized as one of the most comprehensive and useful texts in the field. It contains an immense amount of well-presented, fundamental material, including chapters on vector functions, ordinary differential equations, special functions, calculus of variations, etc., which are excellent introductions to these areas. For students with only one year of calculus, more than 1300 exercises cover both pure math and applications to engineering and physical problems. For engineers, physicists, etc., this work, with its 54 page introductory review, is the ideal reference and refresher. Index. ix + 566pp. 5⅜ x 8.
S504 Paperbound **$2.45**

ELLIPTIC INTEGRALS, H. Hancock. Invaluable in work involving differential equations containing cubics or quartics under the root sign, where elementary calculus methods are inadequate. Practical solutions to problems that occur in mathematics, engineering, physics: differential equations requiring integration of Lamé's, Briot's, or Bouquet's equations; determination of arc of ellipse, hyperbola, lemiscate; solutions of problems in elastica; motion of a projectile under resistance varying as the cube of the velocity; pendulums; many others. Exposition is in accordance with Legendre-Jacobi theory and includes rigorous discussion of Legendre transformations. 20 figures. 5 place table. Index. 104pp. 5⅛ x 8.
S484 Paperbound **$1.25**

FIVE VOLUME "THEORY OF FUNCTIONS' SET BY KONRAD KNOPP

This five-volume set, prepared by Konrad Knopp, provides a complete and readily followed account of theory of functions. Proofs are given concisely, yet without sacrifice of completeness or rigor. These volumes are used as texts by such universities as M.I.T., University of Chicago, N. Y. City College, and many others. "Excellent introduction . . . remarkably readable, concise, clear, rigorous," JOURNAL OF THE AMERICAN STATISTICAL ASSOCIATION.

ELEMENTS OF THE THEORY OF FUNCTIONS, Konrad Knopp. This book provides the student with background for further volumes in this set, or texts on a similar level. Partial contents: foundations, system of complex numbers and the Gaussian plane of numbers, Riemann sphere of numbers, mapping by linear functions, normal forms, the logarithm, the cyclometric functions and binomial series. "Not only for the young student, but also for the student who knows all about what is in it," MATHEMATICAL JOURNAL. Bibliography. Index. 140pp. 5⅜ x 8. S154 Paperbound **$1.35**

THEORY OF FUNCTIONS, PART I, Konrad Knopp. With volume II, this book provides coverage of basic concepts and theorems. Partial contents: numbers and points, functions of a complex variable, integral of a continuous function, Cauchy's integral theorem, Cauchy's integral formulae, series with variable terms, expansion of analytic functions in power series, analytic continuation and complete definition of analytic functions, entire transcendental functions, Laurent expansion, types of singularities. Bibliography. Index. vii + 146pp. 5⅜ x 8.
S156 Paperbound **$1.35**

THEORY OF FUNCTIONS, PART II, Konrad Knopp. Application and further development of general theory, special topics. Single valued functions, entire, Weierstrass, Meromorphic functions. Riemann surfaces. Algebraic functions. Analytical configuration, Riemann surface. Bibliography. Index. x + 150pp. 5⅜ x 8. S157 Paperbound **$1.35**

PROBLEM BOOK IN THE THEORY OF FUNCTIONS, VOLUME 1, Konrad Knopp. Problems in elementary theory, for use with Knopp's THEORY OF FUNCTIONS, or any other text, arranged according to increasing difficulty. Fundamental concepts, sequences of numbers and infinite series, complex variable, integral theorems, development in series, conformal mapping. 182 problems. Answers. viii + 126pp. 5⅜ x 8. S158 Paperbound **$1.35**

PROBLEM BOOK IN THE THEORY OF FUNCTIONS, VOLUME 2, Konrad Knopp. Advanced theory of functions, to be used either with Knopp's THEORY OF FUNCTIONS, or any other comparable text. Singularities, entire & meromorphic functions, periodic, analytic, continuation, multiple-valued functions, Riemann surfaces, conformal mapping. Includes a section of additional elementary problems. "The difficult task of selecting from the immense material of the modern theory of functions the problems just within the reach of the beginner is here masterfully accomplished," AM. MATH. SOC. Answers. 138pp. 5⅜ x 8. S159 Paperbound **$1.35**

* * *

LECTURES ON THE THEORY OF ELLIPTIC FUNCTIONS, H. Hancock. Reissue of the only book in English with so extensive a coverage, especially of Abel, Jacobi, Legendre, Weierstrasse, Hermite, Liouville, and Riemann. Unusual fullness of treatment, plus applications as well as theory, in discussing elliptic function (the universe of elliptic integrals originating in works of Abel and Jacobi), their existence, and ultimate meaning. Use is made of Riemann to provide the most general theory. 40 page table of formulas. 76 figures. xxiii + 498pp.
S483 Paperbound **$2.55**

THE THEORY AND FUNCTIONS OF A REAL VARIABLE AND THE THEORY OF FOURIER'S SERIES, E. W. Hobson. One of the best introductions to set theory and various aspects of functions and Fourier's series. Requires only a good background in calculus. Provides an exhaustive coverage of: metric and descriptive properties of sets of points; transfinite numbers and order types; functions of a real variable; the Riemann and Lebesgue integrals; sequences and series of numbers; power-series; functions representable by series sequences of continuous functions; trigonometrical series; representation of functions by Fourier's series; complete exposition (200pp.) on set theory; and much more. "The best possible guide," Nature. Vol. I: 88 detailed examples, 10 figures. Index. xv + 736pp. Vol. II: 117 detailed examples, 13 figures. Index. x + 780pp. 6⅛ x 9¼. Vol. I: S387 Paperbound **$3.00**
Vol. II: S388 Paperbound **$3.00**

ALMOST PERIODIC FUNCTIONS, A. S. Besicovitch. This unique and important summary by a well-known mathematician covers in detail the two stages of development in Bohr's theory of almost periodic functions: (1) as a generalization of pure periodicity, with results and proofs; (2) the work done by Stepanoff, Wiener, Weyl, and Bohr in generalizing the theory. Bibliography. xi + 180pp. 5⅜ x 8. S18 Paperbound **$1.75**

THEORY OF FUNCTIONALS AND OF INTEGRAL AND INTEGRO-DIFFERENTIAL EQUATIONS, Vito Volterra. Unabridged republication of the only English translation. An exposition of the general theory of the functions depending on a continuous set of values of another function, based on the author's fundamental notion of the transition from a finite number of variables to a continually infinite number. Though dealing primarily with integral equations, much material on calculus of variations is included. The work makes no assumption of previous knowledge on the part of the reader. It begins with fundamental material and proceeds to Generalization of Analytic Functions, Integro-Differential Equations, Functional Derivative Equations, Applications, Other Directions of Theory of Functionals, etc. New introduction by G. C. Evans. Bibliography and criticism of Volterra's work by E. Whittaker. Bibliography. Index of authors cited. Index of subjects. xxxx + 226pp. 5⅜ x 8. S502 Paperbound **$1.75**

AN ELEMENTARY TREATISE ON ELLIPTIC FUNCTIONS, A. Cayley. Still the fullest and clearest text on the theories of Jacobi and Legendre for the advanced student (and an excellent supplement for the beginner). A masterpiece of exposition by the great 19th century British mathematician (creator of the theory of matrices and abstract geometry), it covers the addition-theory, Landen's theorem, the 3 kinds of elliptic integrals, transformations, the q-functions, reduction of a differential expression, and much more. Index. xii + 386pp. 5⅜ x 8. S728 Paperbound **$2.00**

THE APPLICATIONS OF ELLIPTIC FUNCTIONS, A. G. Greenhill. Modern books forgo detail for sake of brevity—this book offers complete exposition necessary for proper understanding, use of elliptic integrals. Formulas developed from definite physical, geometric problems; examples representative enough to offer basic information in widely useable form. Elliptic integrals, addition theorem, algebraical form of addition theorem, elliptic integrals of 2nd, 3rd kind, double periodicity, resolution into factors, series, transformation, etc. Introduction. Index. 25 illus. xi + 357pp. 5⅜ x 8. S603 Paperbound **$1.75**

THE THEORY OF FUNCTIONS OF REAL VARIABLES, James Pierpont. A 2-volume authoritative exposition, by one of the foremost mathematicians of his time. Each theorem stated with all conditions, then followed by proof. No need to go through complicated reasoning to discover conditions added without specific mention. Includes a particularly complete, rigorous presentation of theory of measure; and Pierpont's own work on a theory of Lebesgue integrals, and treatment of area of a curved surface. Partial contents, Vol. 1: rational numbers, exponentials, logarithms, point aggregates, maxima, minima, proper integrals, improper integrals, multiple proper integrals, continuity, discontinuity, indeterminate forms. Vol. 2: point sets, proper integrals, series, power series, aggregates, ordinal numbers, discontinuous functions, sub-, infra-uniform convergence, much more. Index. 95 illustrations. 1229pp. 5⅜ x 8. S558-9, 2 volume set, paperbound **$4.90**

FUNCTIONS OF A COMPLEX VARIABLE, James Pierpont. Long one of best in the field. A thorough treatment of fundamental elements, concepts, theorems. A complete study, rigorous, detailed, with carefully selected problems worked out to illustrate each topic. Partial contents: arithmetical operations, real term series, positive term series, exponential functions, integration, analytic functions, asymptotic expansions, functions of Weierstrass, Legendre, etc. Index. List of symbols. 122 illus. 597pp. 5⅜ x 8. S560 Paperbound **$2.45**

ELEMENTS OF THE THEORY OF REAL FUNCTIONS, J. E. Littlewood. Based on lectures given at Trinity College, Cambridge, this book has proved to be extremely successful in introducing graduate students to the modern theory of functions. It offers a full and concise coverage of classes and cardinal numbers, well-ordered series, other types of series, and elements of the theory of sets of points. 3rd revised edition. vii + 71pp. 5⅜ x 8.
S171 Clothbound **$2.85**
S172 Paperbound **$1.25**

TRANSCENDENTAL AND ALGEBRAIC NUMBERS, A. O. Gelfond. First English translation of work by leading Soviet mathematician. Thue-Siegel theorem, its p-adic analogue, on approximation of algebraic numbers by numbers in fixed algebraic field; Hermite-Lindemann theorem on transcendency of Bessel functions, solutions of other differential equations; Gelfond-Schneider theorem on transcendency of alpha to power beta; Schneider's work on elliptic functions, with method developed by Gelfond. Translated by L. F. Boron. Index. Bibliography. 200pp. 5⅜ x 8. S615 Paperbound **$1.75**

THEORY OF MAXIMA AND MINIMA, H. Hancock. Fullest treatment ever written; only work in English with extended discussion of maxima and minima for functions of 1, 2, or n variables, problems with subsidiary constraints, and relevant quadratic forms. Detailed proof of each important theorem. Covers the Scheeffer and von Dantscher theories, homogeneous quadratic forms, reversion of series, fallacious establishment of maxima and minima, etc. Unsurpassed treatise for advanced students of calculus, mathematicians, economists, statisticians. Index. 24 diagrams. 39 problems, many examples. 193pp. 5⅜ x 8. S665 Paperbound **$1.50**

DICTIONARY OF CONFORMAL REPRESENTATIONS, H. Kober. Laplace's equation in 2 dimensions solved in this unique book developed by the British Admiralty. Scores of geometrical forms & their transformations for electrical engineers, Joukowski aerofoil for aerodynamists. Schwartz-Christoffel transformations for hydrodynamics, transcendental functions. Contents classified according to analytical functions describing transformation. Twin diagrams show curves of most transformations with corresponding regions. Glossary. Topological index. 447 diagrams. 244pp. 6⅛ x 9¼. S160 Paperbound **$2.00**

THE TAYLOR SERIES, AN INTRODUCTION TO THE THEORY OF FUNCTIONS OF A COMPLEX VARIABLE, P. Dienes. This book investigates the entire realm of analytic functions. Only ordinary calculus is needed, except in the last two chapters. Starting with an introduction to real variables and complex algebra, the properties of infinite series, elementary functions, complex differentiation and integration are carefully derived. Also biuniform mapping, a thorough two part discussion of representation and singularities of analytic functions, overconvergence and gap theorems, divergent series, Taylor series on its circle of convergence, divergence and singularities, etc. Unabridged, corrected reissue of first edition. Preface and index. 186 examples, many fully worked out. 67 figures. xii + 555pp. 5⅜ x 8.
S391 Paperbound **$2.75**

INTRODUCTION TO BESSEL FUNCTIONS, Frank Bowman. A rigorous self-contained exposition providing all necessary material during the development, which requires only some knowledge of calculus and acquaintance with differential equations. A balanced presentation including applications and practical use. Discusses Bessel Functions of Zero Order, of Any Real Order; Modified Bessel Functions of Zero Order; Definite Integrals; Asymptotic Expansions; Bessel's Solution to Kepler's Problem; Circular Membranes; much more. "Clear and straightforward . . . useful not only to students of physics and engineering, but to mathematical students in general," Nature. 226 problems. Short tables of Bessel functions. 27 figures. Index. x + 135pp. 5⅜ x 8.
S462 Paperbound **$1.35**

MODERN THEORIES OF INTEGRATION, H. Kestelman. Connected and concrete coverage, with fully-worked-out proofs for every step. Ranges from elementary definitions through theory of aggregates, sets of points, Riemann and Lebesgue integration, and much more. This new revised and enlarged edition contains a new chapter on Riemann-Stieltjes integration, as well as a supplementary section of 186 exercises. Ideal for the mathematician, student, teacher, or self-studier. Index of Definitions and Symbols. General Index. Bibliography. x + 310pp. 5⅝ x 8⅜.
S572 Paperbound **$2.00**

A TREATISE ON THE THEORY OF DETERMINANTS, T. Muir. Unequalled as an exhaustive compilation of nearly all the known facts about determinants up to the early 1930's. Covers notation and general properties, row and column transformation, symmetry, compound determinants, adjugates, rectangular arrays and matrices, linear dependence, gradients, Jacobians, Hessians, Wronskians, and much more. Invaluable for libraries of industrial and research organizations as well as for student, teacher, and mathematician; very useful in the field of computing machines. Revised and enlarged by W. H. Metzler. Index. 485 problems and scores of numerical examples. iv + 766pp. 5⅜ x 8.
S670 Paperbound **$2.95**

THEORY OF DETERMINANTS IN THE HISTORICAL ORDER OF DEVELOPMENT, Sir Thomas Muir. Unabridged reprinting of this complete study of 1,859 papers on determinant theory written between 1693 and 1900. Most important and original sections reproduced, valuable commentary on each. No other work is necessary for determinant research: all types are covered—each subdivision of the theory treated separately; all papers dealing with each type are covered; you are told exactly what each paper is about and how important its contribution is. Each result, theory, extension, or modification is assigned its own identifying numeral so that the full history may be more easily followed. Includes papers on determinants in general, determinants and linear equations, symmetric determinants, alternants, recurrents, determinants having invariant factors, and all other major types. "A model of what such histories ought to be," NATURE. "Mathematicians must ever be grateful to Sir Thomas for his monumental work," AMERICAN MATH MONTHLY. Four volumes bound as two. Indices. Bibliographies. Total of lxxxiv + 1977pp. 5⅜ x 8.
S672-3 The set, Clothbound **$10.00**

A COURSE IN MATHEMATICAL ANALYSIS, Edouard Goursat. Trans. by E. R. Hedrick, O. Dunkel. Classic study of fundamental material thoroughly treated. Exceptionally lucid exposition of wide range of subject matter for student with 1 year of calculus. Vol. 1: Derivatives and Differentials, Definite Integrals, Expansion in Series, Applications to Geometry. Problems. Index. 52 illus. 556pp. Vol. 2, Part I: Functions of a Complex Variable, Conformal Representations, Doubly Periodic Functions, Natural Boundaries, etc. Problems. Index. 38 illus. 269pp. Vol. 2, Part 2: Differential Equations, Cauchy-Lipschitz Method, Non-linear Differential Equations, Simultaneous Equations, etc. Problems. Index. 308pp. 5⅜ x 8.
Vol. 1 S554 Paperbound **$2.25**
Vol. 2 part 1 S555 Paperbound **$1.65**
Vol. 2 part 2 S556 Paperbound **$1.65**
3 vol. set **$5.00**

INFINITE SEQUENCES AND SERIES, Konrad Knopp. First publication in any language! Excellent introduction to 2 topics of modern mathematics, designed to give the student background to penetrate farther by himself. Sequences & sets, real & complex numbers, etc. Functions of a real & complex variable. Sequences & series. Infinite series. Convergent power series. Expansion of elementary functions. Numerical evaluation of series. Bibliography. v + 186pp. 5⅜ x 8.
S152 Clothbound **$3.50**
S153 Paperbound **$1.75**

TRIGONOMETRICAL SERIES, Antoni Zygmund. Unique in any language on modern advanced level. Contains carefully organized analyses of trigonometric, orthogonal, Fourier systems of functions, with clear adequate descriptions of summability of Fourier series, proximation theory, conjugate series, convergence, divergence of Fourier series. Especially valuable for Russian, Eastern European coverage. Bibliography. 329pp. 5⅜ x 8.
S290 Paperbound **$1.50**

COLLECTED WORKS OF BERNHARD RIEMANN. This important source book is the first to contain the complete text of both 1892 Werke and the 1902 supplement, unabridged. It contains 31 monographs, 3 complete lecture courses, 15 miscellaneous papers, which have been of enormous importance in relativi'y, topology, theory of complex variables, and other areas of mathematics. Edited by R. Dedekind, H. Weber, M. Noether, W. Wirtinger. German text. English introduction by Hans Lewy. 690pp. 5⅜ x 8. S226 Paperbound **$2.85**

See also: **A HISTORY OF THE CALCULUS, C. B. Boyer; CALCULUS REFRESHER FOR TECHNICAL MEN, A. A. Klaf; MONOGRAPHS ON TOPICS OF MODERN MATHEMATICS, ed. by J. W. A. Young; THE CONTINUUM AND OTHER TYPES OF SERIAL ORDER, E. V. Huntington.**

Symbolic logic

AN INTRODUCTION TO SYMBOLIC LOGIC, Susanne K. Langer. Probably the clearest book ever written on symbolic logic for the philosopher, general scientist and layman. It will be particularly appreciated by those who have been rebuffed by other introductory works because of insufficient mathematical training. No special knowledge of mathematics is required. Starting with the simplest symbols and conventions, you are led to a remarkable grasp of the Boole-Schroeder and Russell-Whitehead systems clearly and quickly. PARTIAL CONTENTS: Study of forms, Essentials of logical structure, Generalization, Classes, The deductive system of classes, The algebra of logic, Abstraction of interpretation, Calculus of propositions, Assumptions of PRINCIPIA MATHEMATICA, Logistics, Logic of the syllogism, Proofs of theorems. "One of the clearest and simplest introductions to a subject which is very much alive. The style is easy, symbolism is introduced gradually, and the intelligent non-mathematician should have no difficulty in following the argument," MATHEMATICS GAZETTE. Revised, expanded second edition. Truth-value tables. 368pp. 5⅜ x 8.
S164 Paperbound **$1.75**

THE ELEMENTS OF MATHEMATICAL LOGIC, Paul Rosenbloom. First publication in any language. This book is intended for readers who are mature mathematically, but have no previous training in symbolic logic. It does not limit itself to a single system, but covers the field as a whole. It is a development of lectures given at Lund University, Sweden, in 1948. Partial contents: Logic of classes, fundamental theorems, Boolean algebra, logic of propositions, logic of propositional functions, expressive languages, combinatory logics, development of mathematics within an object language, paradoxes, theorems of Post and Goedel, Church's theorem, and similar topics. iv + 214pp. 5⅜ x 8. S227 Paperbound **$1.45**

A SURVEY OF SYMBOLIC LOGIC: THE CLASSIC ALGEBRA OF LOGIC, C. I. Lewis. Classic survey of the field, comprehensive and thorough. Indicates content of major systems, alternative methods of procedure, and relation of these to the Boole-Schroeder algebra and to one another. Contains historical summary, as well as full proofs and applications of the classic, or Boole-Schroeder, algebra of logic. Discusses diagrams for the logical relations of classes, the two-valued algebra, propositional functions of two or more variables, etc. Chapters 5 and 6 of the original edition, which contained material not directly pertinent, have been omitted in this edition at the author's request. Appendix. Bibliography. Index. viii + 352pp. 5⅝ x 8⅜.
S643 Paperbound **$2.00**

INTRODUCTION TO SYMBOLIC LOGIC AND ITS APPLICATIONS, R. Carnap. One of the clearest, most comprehensive, and rigorous introductions to modern symbolic logic by perhaps its greatest living master. Symbolic languages are analyzed and one constructed. Applications to math (symbolic representation of axiom systems for set theory, natural numbers, real numbers, topology, Dedekind and Cantor explanations of continuity), physics (the general analysis of concepts of determination, causality, space-time-topology, based on Einstein), biology (symbolic representation of an axiom system for basic concepts). "A masterpiece," Zentralblatt für Mathematik und ihre Grenzgebiete. Over 300 exercises. 5 figures. Bibliography. Index. xvi + 241pp. 5⅜ x 8. S453 Paperbound **$1.85**
Clothbound **$4.00**

SYMBOLIC LOGIC, C. I. Lewis, C. H. Langford. Probably the most cited book in symbolic logic, this is one of the fullest treatments of paradoxes. A wide coverage of the entire field of symbolic logic, plus considerable material that has not appeared elsewhere. Basic to the entire volume is the distinction between the logic of extensions and of intensions. Considerable emphasis is placed on converse substitution, while the matrix system presents the supposition of a variety of non-Aristotelian logics. It has especially valuable sections on strict limitations, existence of terms, 2-valued algebra and its extension to propositional functions, truth value systems, the matrix method, implication and deductibility, general theory of propositions, propositions of ordinary discourse, and similar topics. "Authoritative, most valuable," TIMES, London. Bibliography. 506pp. 5⅜ x 8. S170 Paperbound **$2.00**

THE LAWS OF THOUGHT, George Boole. This book founded symbolic logic some hundred years ago. It is the 1st significant attempt to apply logic to all aspects of human endeavour. Partial contents: derivation of laws, signs & laws, interpretations, eliminations, conditions of a perfect method, analysis, Aristotelian logic, probability, and similar topics. xviii + 424pp. 5⅜ x 8. S28 Paperbound **$2.00**

THE PRINCIPLES OF SCIENCE, A TREATISE ON LOGIC AND THE SCIENTIFIC METHOD, W. S. Jevons. Treating such topics as Inductive and Deductive Logic, the Theory of Number, Probability, and the Limits of Scientific Method, this milestone in the development of symbolic logic remains a stimulating contribution to the investigation of inferential validity in the natural and social sciences. It significantly advances Boole's logic, and contains a detailed introduction to the nature and methods of probability in physics, astronomy, everyday affairs, etc. In his introduction, Ernest Nagel of Columbia University says, "[Jevons] continues to be of interest as an attempt to articulate the logic of scientific inquiry." Index. liii + 786pp. 5⅜ x 8. S446 Paperbound **$2.98**

Group theory, algebra, sets

LECTURES ON THE ICOSAHEDRON AND THE SOLUTION OF EQUATIONS OF THE FIFTH DEGREE, Felix Klein. The solution of quintics in terms of rotation of a regular icosahedron around its axes of symmetry. A classic & indispensable source for those interested in higher algebra, geometry, crystallography. Considerable explanatory material included. 230 footnotes, mostly bibliographic. 2nd edition, xvi + 289pp. 5⅜ x 8. S314 Paperbound **$1.85**

LINEAR GROUPS, WITH AN EXPOSITION OF THE GALOIS FIELD THEORY, L. E. Dickson. The classic exposition of the theory of groups, well within the range of the graduate student. Part I contains the most extensive and thorough presentation of the theory of Galois Fields available, with a wealth of examples and theorems. Part II is a full discussion of linear groups of finite order. Much material in this work is based on Dickson's own contributions. Also includes expositions of Jordan, Lie, Abel, Betti-Mathieu, Hermite, etc. "A milestone in the development of modern algebra," W. Magnus, in his historical introduction to this edition. Index. xv + 312pp. 5⅜ x 8. S482 Paperbound **$1.95**

INTRODUCTION TO THE THEORY OF GROUPS OF FINITE ORDER, R. Carmichael. Examines fundamental theorems and their application. Beginning with sets, systems, permutations, etc., it progresses in easy stages through important types of groups: Abelian, prime power, permutation, etc. Except 1 chapter where matrices are desirable, no higher math needed. 783 exercises, problems. Index. xvi + 447pp. 5⅜ x 8. S299 Clothbound **$3.95**
S300 Paperbound **$2.00**

THEORY OF GROUPS OF FINITE ORDER, W. Burnside. First published some 40 years ago, this is still one of the clearest introductory texts. Partial contents: permutations, groups independent of representation, composition series of a group, isomorphism of a group with itself, Abelian groups, prime power groups, permutation groups, invariants of groups of linear substitution graphical representation, etc. 45pp. of notes. Indexes. xxiv + 512pp. 5⅜ x 8.
S38 Paperbound **$2.45**

THEORY AND APPLICATIONS OF FINITE GROUPS, G. A. Miller, H. F. Blichfeldt, L. E. Dickson. Unusually accurate and authoritative work, each section prepared by a leading specialist: Miller on substitution and abstract groups, Blichfeldt on finite groups of linear homogeneous transformations, Dickson on applications of finite groups. Unlike more modern works, this gives the concrete basis from which abstract group theory arose. Includes Abelian groups, prime-power groups, isomorphisms, matrix forms of linear transformations, Sylow groups, Galois' theory of algebraic equations, duplication of a cube, trisection of an angle, etc. 2 Indexes. 267 problems. xvii + 390pp. 5⅜ x 8. S216 Paperbound **$2.00**

CONTINUOUS GROUPS OF TRANSFORMATIONS, L. P. Eisenhart. Intensive study of the theory and geometrical applications of continuous groups of transformations; a standard work on the subject, called forth by the revolution in physics in the 1920's. Covers tensor analysis, Riemannian geometry, canonical parameters, transitivity, imprimitivity, differential invariants, the algebra of constants of structure, differential geometry, contact transformations, etc. "Likely to remain one of the standard works on the subject for many years . . . principal theorems are proved clearly and concisely, and the arrangement of the whole is coherent," MATHEMATICAL GAZETTE. Index. 72-item bibliography. 185 exercises. ix + 301pp. 5⅜ x 8.
S781 Paperbound **$1.85**

THE THEORY OF GROUPS AND QUANTUM MECHANICS, H. Weyl. Discussions of Schroedinger's wave equation, de Broglie's waves of a particle, Jordan-Hoelder theorem, Lie's continuous groups of transformations, Pauli exclusion principle, quantization of Maxwell-Dirac field equations, etc. Unitary geometry, quantum theory, groups, application of groups to quantum mechanics, symmetry permutation group, algebra of symmetric transformation, etc. 2nd revised edition. Bibliography. Index. xxii + 422pp. 5⅜ x 8. S268 Clothbound **$4.50**
S269 Paperbound **$1.95**

ALGEBRAIC THEORIES, L. E. Dickson. Best thorough introduction to classical topics in higher algebra develops theories centering around matrices, invariants, groups. Higher algebra, Galois theory, finite linear groups, Klein's icosahedron, algebraic invariants, linear transformations, elementary divisors, invariant factors; quadratic, bi-linear, Hermitian forms, singly and in pairs. Proofs rigorous, detailed; topics developed lucidly, in close connection with their most frequent mathematical applications. Formerly "Modern Algebraic Theories." 155 problems. Bibliography. 2 indexes. 285pp. 5⅜ x 8. S547 Paperbound **$1.50**

ALGEBRAS AND THEIR ARITHMETICS, L. E. Dickson. Provides the foundation and background necessary to any advanced undergraduate or graduate student studying abstract algebra. Begins with elementary introduction to linear transformations, matrices, field of complex numbers; proceeds to order, basal units, modulus, quaternions, etc.; develops calculus of linear sets, describes various examples of algebras including invariant, difference, nilpotent, semi-simple. "Makes the reader marvel at his genius for clear and profound analysis," Amer. Mathematical Monthly. Index. xii + 241pp. 5⅜ x 8. S616 Paperbound **$1.35**

THE THEORY OF EQUATIONS WITH AN INTRODUCTION TO THE THEORY OF BINARY ALGEBRAIC FORMS, W. S. Burnside and A. W. Panton. Extremely thorough and concrete discussion of the theory of equations, with extensive detailed treatment of many topics curtailed in later texts. Covers theory of algebraic equations, properties of polynomials, symmetric functions, derived functions, Horner's process, complex numbers and the complex variable, determinants and methods of elimination, invariant theory (nearly 100 pages), transformations, introduction to Galois theory, Abelian equations, and much more. Invaluable supplementary work for modern students and teachers. 759 examples and exercises. Index in each volume. Two volume set. Total of xxiv + 604pp. 5⅜ x 8. S714 Vol I Paperbound **$1.85**
S715 Vol II Paperbound **$1.85**
The set **$3.70**

COMPUTATIONAL METHODS OF LINEAR ALGEBRA, V. N. Faddeeva, translated by **C. D. Benster.** First English translation of a unique and valuable work, the only work in English presenting a systematic exposition of the most important methods of linear algebra—classical and contemporary. Shows in detail how to derive numerical solutions of problems in mathematical physics which are frequently connected with those of linear algebra. Theory as well as individual practice. Part I surveys the mathematical background that is indispensable to what follows. Parts II and III, the conclusion, set forth the most important methods of solution, for both exact and iterative groups. One of the most outstanding and valuable features of this work is the 23 tables, double and triple checked for accuracy. These tables will not be found elsewhere. Author's preface. Translator's note. New bibliography and index. x + 252pp. 5⅜ x 8. S424 Paperbound **$1.95**

ALGEBRAIC EQUATIONS, E. Dehn. Careful and complete presentation of Galois' theory of algebraic equations; theories of Lagrange and Galois developed in logical rather than historical form, with a more thorough exposition than in most modern books. Many concrete applications and fully-worked-out examples. Discusses basic theory (very clear exposition of the symmetric group); isomorphic, transitive, and Abelian groups; applications of Lagrange's and Galois' theories; and much more. Newly revised by the author. Index. List of Theorems. xi + 208pp. 5⅜ x 8. S697 Paperbound **$1.45**

THEORY OF SETS, E. Kamke. Clearest, amplest introduction in English, well suited for independent study. Subdivision of main theory, such as theory of sets of points, are discussed, but emphasis is on general theory. Partial contents: rudiments of set theory, arbitrary sets and their cardinal numbers, ordered sets and their order types, well-ordered sets and their cardinal numbers. Bibliography. Key to symbols. Index. vii + 144pp. 5⅜ x 8. S141 Paperbound **$1.35**

Number theory

INTRODUCTION TO THE THEORY OF NUMBERS, L. E. Dickson. Thorough, comprehensive approach with adequate coverage of classical literature, an introductory volume beginners can follow. Chapters on divisibility, congruences, quadratic residues & reciprocity, Diophantine equations, etc. Full treatment of binary quadratic forms without usual restriction to integral coefficients. Covers infinitude of primes, least residues, Fermat's theorem, Euler's phi function, Legendre's symbol, Gauss's lemma, automorphs, reduced forms, recent theorems of Thue & Siegel, many more. Much material not readily available elsewhere. 239 problems. Index. I figure. viii + 183pp. 5⅜ x 8. S342 Paperbound **$1.65**

ELEMENTS OF NUMBER THEORY, I. M. Vinogradov. Detailed 1st course for persons without advanced mathematics; 95% of this book can be understood by readers who have gone no farther than high school algebra. Partial contents: divisibility theory, important number theoretical functions, congruences, primitive roots and indices, etc. Solutions to both problems and exercises. Tables of primes, indices, etc. Covers almost every essential formula in elementary number theory! Translated from Russian. 233 problems, 104 exercises. viii + 227pp. 5⅜ x 8. S259 Paperbound **$1.60**

THEORY OF NUMBERS and DIOPHANTINE ANALYSIS, R. D. Carmichael. These two complete works in one volume form one of the most lucid introductions to number theory, requiring only a firm foundation in high school mathematics. "Theory of Numbers," partial contents: Eratosthenes' sieve, Euclid's fundamental theorem, G.C.F. and L.C.M. of two or more integers, linear congruences, etc "Diophantine Analysis": rational triangles, Pythagorean triangles, equations of third, fourth, higher degrees, method of functional equations, much more. "Theory of Numbers": 76 problems. Index. 94pp. "Diophantine Analysis": 222 problems. Index. 118pp. 5⅜ x 8. S529 Paperbound **$1.35**

CONTRIBUTIONS TO THE FOUNDING OF THE THEORY OF TRANSFINITE NUMBERS, Georg Cantor. These papers founded a new branch of mathematics. The famous articles of 1895-7 are translated, with an 82-page introduction by P. E. B. Jourdain dealing with Cantor, the background of his discoveries, their results, future possibilities. Bibliography. Index. Notes. ix + 211 pp. 5⅜ x 8. S45 Paperbound **$1.25**

See also: **TRANSCENDENTAL AND ALGEBRAIC NUMBERS, A. O. Gelfond.**

Probability theory and information theory

A PHILOSOPHICAL ESSAY ON PROBABILITIES, Marquis de Laplace. This famous essay explains without recourse to mathematics the principle of probability, and the application of probability to games of chance, natural philosophy, astronomy, many other fields. Translated from the 6th French edition by F. W. Truscott, F. L. Emory, with new introduction for this edition by E. T. Bell. 204pp. 5⅜ x 8. S166 Paperbound **$1.35**

MATHEMATICAL FOUNDATIONS OF INFORMATION THEORY, A. I. Khinchin. For the first time mathematicians, statisticians, physicists, cyberneticists, and communications engineers are offered a complete and exact introduction to this relatively new field. Entropy as a measure of a finite scheme, applications to coding theory, study of sources, channels and codes, detailed proofs of both Shannon theorems for any ergodic source and any stationary channel with finite memory, and much more are covered. Bibliography. vii + 120pp. 5⅜ x 8. S434 Paperbound **$1.35**

SELECTED PAPERS ON NOISE AND STOCHASTIC PROCESS, edited by **Prof. Nelson Wax,** U. of Illinois. 6 basic papers for newcomers in the field, for those whose work involves noise characteristics. Chandrasekhar, Uhlenbeck & Ornstein, Uhlenbeck & Ming, Rice, Doob. Included is Kac's Chauvenet-Prize winning Random Walk. Extensive bibliography lists 200 articles, up through 1953. 21 figures. 337pp. 6⅛ x 9¼. S262 Paperbound **$2.35**

THEORY OF PROBABILITY, William Burnside. Synthesis, expansion of individual papers presents numerous problems in classical probability, offering many original views succinctly, effectively. Game theory, cards, selections from groups; geometrical probability in such areas as suppositions as to probability of position of point on a line, points on surface of sphere, etc. Includes methods of approximation, theory of errors, direct calculation of probabilities, etc. Index. 136pp. 5⅜ x 8. S567 Paperbound **$1.00**

Vector and tensor analysis, matrix theory

VECTOR AND TENSOR ANALYSIS, A. P. Wills. Covers the entire field of vector and tensor analysis from elementary notions to dyads and non-Euclidean manifolds (especially detailed), absolute differentiation, the Lamé operator, the Riemann-Christoffel and Ricci-Einstein tensors, and the calculation of the Gaussian curvature of a surface. Many illustrations from electrical engineering, relativity theory, astro-physics, quantum mechanics. Presupposes only a good working knowledge of calculus. Exercises at end of each chapter. Intended for physicists and engineers as well as pure mathematicians. 44 diagrams. 114 problems. Bibliography. Index. xxxii + 285pp. 5⅜ x 8. S454 Paperbound **$1.75**

APPLICATIONS OF TENSOR ANALYSIS, A. J. McConnell. (Formerly APPLICATIONS OF THE ABSOLUTE DIFFERENTIAL CALCULUS.) An excellent text for understanding the application of tensor methods to familiar subjects such as dynamics, electricity, elasticity, and hydrodynamics. Explains the fundamental ideas and notation of tensor theory, the geometrical treatment of tensor algebra, the theory of differentiation of tensors, and includes a wealth of practical material. Bibliography. Index. 43 illustrations. 685 problems. xii + 381pp. 5⅜ x 8. S373 Paperbound **$1.85**

VECTOR AND TENSOR ANALYSIS, G. E. Hay. One of the clearest introductions to this increasingly important subject. Start with simple definitions, finish the book with a sure mastery of oriented Cartesian vectors, Christoffel symbols, solenoidal tensors, and their applications. Complete breakdown of plane, solid, analytical, differential geometry. Separate chapters on application. All fundamental formulae listed & demonstrated. 195 problems, 66 figures. viii + 193pp. 5⅜ x 8. S109 Paperbound **$1.75**

VECTOR ANALYSIS, FOUNDED UPON THE LECTURES OF J. WILLARD GIBBS, by E. B. Wilson. Still a first-rate introduction and supplementary text for students of mathematics and physics. Based on the pioneering lectures of Yale's great J. Willard Gibbs, can be followed by anyone who has had some calculus. Practical approach, stressing efficient use of combinations and functions of vectors. Worked examples from geometry, mechanics, hydrodynamics, gas theory, etc., as well as practice examples. Covers basic vector processes, differential and integral calculus in relation to vector functions, and theory of linear vector functions, forming an introduction to the study of multiple algebra and matrix theory. While the notation is not always modern, it is easily followed. xviii + 436pp. 5⅜ x 8. S656 Paperbound **$2.00**

PROBLEMS AND WORKED SOLUTIONS IN VECTOR ANALYSIS, L. R. Shorter. More pages of fully-worked-out examples than any other text on vector analysis. A self-contained course for home study or a fine classroom supplement. 138 problems and examples begin with fundamentals, then cover systems of coordinates, relative velocity and acceleration, the commutative and distributive laws, axial and polar vectors, finite displacements, the calculus of vectors, curl and divergence, etc. Final chapter treats applications in dynamics and physics: kinematics of a rigid body, equipotential surfaces, etc. "Very helpful . . . very comprehensive. A handy book like this . . . will fill a great want," MATHEMATICAL GAZETTE. Index. List of 174 important equations. 158 figures. xiv + 356pp. 5⅜ x 8. S135 Paperbound **$2.00**

THE THEORY OF DETERMINANTS, MATRICES, AND INVARIANTS, H. W. Turnbull. 3rd revised, corrected edition of this important study of virtually all the salient features and major theories of the subject. Covers Laplace identities, linear equations, differentiation, symbolic and direct methods for the reduction of invariants, seminvariants, Hilbert's Basis Theorem, Clebsch's Theorem, canonical forms, etc. New appendix contains a proof of Jacobi's lemma, further properties of symmetric determinants, etc. More than 350 problems. New references to recent developments. xviii + 374pp. 5⅜ x 8. S699 Paperbound **$2.00**

Differential equations, ordinary and partial, and integral equations

INTRODUCTION TO THE DIFFERENTIAL EQUATIONS OF PHYSICS, L. Hopf. Especially valuable to the engineer with no math beyond elementary calculus. Emphasizing intuitive rather than formal aspects of concepts, the author covers an extensive territory. Partial contents: Law of causality, energy theorem, damped oscillations, coupling by friction, cylindrical and spherical coordinates, heat source, etc. Index. 48 figures. 160pp. 5⅜ x 8. S120 Paperbound **$1.25**

INTRODUCTION TO THE THEORY OF LINEAR DIFFERENTIAL EQUATIONS, E. G. Poole. Authoritative discussions of important topics, with methods of solution more detailed than usual, for students with background of elementary course in differential equations. Studies existence theorems, linearly independent solutions; equations with constant coefficients; with uniform analytic coefficients; regular singularities; the hypergeometric equation; conformal representation; etc. Exercises. Index. 210pp. 5⅜ x 8. S629 Paperbound **$1.65**

DIFFERENTIAL EQUATIONS FOR ENGINEERS, P. Franklin. Outgrowth of a course given 10 years at M. I. T. Makes most useful branch of pure math accessible for practical work. Theoretical basis of D.E.'s; solution of ordinary D.E.'s and partial derivatives arising from heat flow, steady-state temperature of a plate, wave equations; analytic functions; convergence of Fourier Series. 400 problems on electricity, vibratory systems, other topics. Formerly "Differential Equations for Electrical Engineers." Index. 41 illus. 307pp. 5⅜ x 8. S601 Paperbound **$1.65**

DIFFERENTIAL EQUATIONS, F. R. Moulton. A detailed, rigorous exposition of all the non-elementary processes of solving ordinary differential equations. Several chapters devoted to the treatment of practical problems, especially those of a physical nature, which are far more advanced than problems usually given as illustrations. Includes analytic differential equations; variations of a parameter; integrals of differential equations; analytic implicit functions; problems of elliptic motion; sine-amplitude functions; deviation of formal bodies; Cauchy-Lipschitz process; linear differential equations with periodic coefficients; differential equations in infinitely many variations; much more. Historical notes. 10 figures. 222 problems. Index. xv + 395pp. 5⅜ x 8. S451 Paperbound **$2.00**

LECTURES ON CAUCHY'S PROBLEM, J. Hadamard. Based on lectures given at Columbia, Rome, this discusses work of Riemann, Kirchhoff, Volterra, and the author's own research on the hyperbolic case in linear partial differential equations. It extends spherical and cylindrical waves to apply to all (normal) hyperbolic equations. Partial contents: Cauchy's problem, fundamental formula, equations with odd number, with even number of independent variables; method of descent. 32 figures. Index. iii + 316pp. 5⅜ x 8. S105 Paperbound **$1.75**

PARTIAL DIFFERENTIAL EQUATIONS OF MATHEMATICAL PHYSICS, A. G. Webster. A keystone work in the library of every mature physicist, engineer, researcher. Valuable sections on elasticity, compression theory, potential theory, theory of sound, heat conduction, wave propagation, vibration theory. Contents include: deduction of differential equations, vibrations, normal functions, Fourier's series, Cauchy's method, boundary problems, method of Riemann-Volterra. Spherical, cylindrical, ellipsoidal harmonics, applications, etc. 97 figures. vii + 440pp. 5⅜ x 8. S263 Paperbound **$2.00**

ORDINARY DIFFERENTIAL EQUATIONS, E. L. Ince. A most compendious analysis in real and complex domains. Existence and nature of solutions, continuous transformation groups, solutions in an infinite form, definite integrals, algebraic theory, Sturmian theory, boundary problems, existence theorems, 1st order, higher order, etc. "Deserves the highest praise, a notable addition to mathematical literature," BULLETIN, AM. MATH. SOC. Historical appendix. Bibliography. 18 figures. viii + 558pp. 5⅜ x 8. S349 Paperbound **$2.55**

THEORY OF DIFFERENTIAL EQUATIONS, A. R. Forsyth. Out of print for over a decade, the complete 6 volumes (now bound as 3) of this monumental work represent the most comprehensive treatment of differential equations ever written. Historical presentation includes in 2500 pages every substantial development. Vol. 1, 2: EXACT EQUATIONS, PFAFF'S PROBLEM; ORDINARY EQUATIONS, NOT LINEAR: methods of Grassmann, Clebsch, Lie, Darboux; Cauchy's theorem; branch points; etc. Vol. 3, 4: ORDINARY EQUATIONS, NOT LINEAR; ORDINARY LINEAR EQUATIONS: Zeta Fuchsian functions, general theorems on algebraic integrals, Brun's theorem, equations with uniform periodic coffiecients, etc. Vol. 4, 5: PARTIAL DIFFERENTIAL EQUATIONS: 2 existence-theorems, equations of theoretical dynamics, Laplace transformations, general transformation of equations of the 2nd order, much more. Indexes. Total of 2766pp. 5⅜ x 8. S576-7-8 Clothbound: the set **$15.00**

DIFFERENTIAL AND INTEGRAL EQUATIONS OF MECHANICS AND PHYSICS (DIE DIFFERENTIAL- UND INTEGRALGLEICHUNGEN DER MECHANIK UND PHYSIK), edited by P. Frank and R. von Mises. Most comprehensive and authoritative work on the mathematics of mathematical physics available today in the United States: the standard, definitive reference for teachers, physicists, engineers, and mathematicians—now published (in the original German) at a relatively inexpensive price for the first time! Every chapter in this 2,000-page set is by an expert in his field: Caratheodory, Courant, Frank, Mises, and a dozen others. Vol. I, on mathematics, gives concise but complete coverages of advanced calculus, differential equations, integral equations, and potential, and partial differential equations. Index. xxiii + 916pp. Vol. II (physics): classical mechanics, optics, continuous mechanics, heat conduction and diffusion, the stationary and quasi-stationary electromagnetic field, electromagnetic oscillations, and wave mechanics. Index. xxiv + 1106pp. Two volume set. Each volume available separately. 5⅝ x 8⅜. S787 Vol I Clothbound **$7.50**
S788 Vol II Clothbound **$7.50**
The set **$15.00**

MATHEMATICAL ANALYSIS OF ELECTRICAL AND OPTICAL WAVE-MOTION, Harry Bateman. Written by one of this century's most distinguished mathematical physicists, this is a practical introduction to those developments of Maxwell's electromagnetic theory which are directly connected with the solution of the partial differential equation of wave motion. Methods of solving wave-equation, polar-cylindrical coordinates, diffraction, transformation of coordinates, homogeneous solutions, electromagnetic fields with moving singularities, etc. Index. 168pp. 5⅜ x 8. S14 Paperbound **$1.60**

See also: **THE ANALYTICAL THEORY OF HEAT, J. Fourier; INTRODUCTION TO BESSEL FUNCTIONS, F. Bowman.**

Statistics

ELEMENTARY STATISTICS, WITH APPLICATIONS IN MEDICINE AND THE BIOLOGICAL SCIENCES, F. E. Croxton. A sound introduction to statistics for anyone in the physical sciences, assuming no prior acquaintance and requiring only a modest knowledge of math. All basic formulas carefully explained and illustrated; all necessary reference tables included. From basic terms and concepts, the study proceeds to frequency distribution, linear, non-linear, and multiple correlation, skewness, kurtosis, etc. A large section deals with reliability and significance of statistical methods. Containing concrete examples from medicine and biology, this book will prove unusually helpful to workers in those fields who increasingly must evaluate, check, and interpret statistics. Formerly titled "Elementary Statistics with Applications in Medicine." 101 charts. 57 tables. 14 appendices. Index. iv + 376pp. 5⅜ x 8.
S506 Paperbound **$1.95**

METHODS OF STATISTICS, L. H. C. Tippett. A classic in its field, this unusually complete systematic introduction to statistical methods begins at beginner's level and progresses to advanced levels for experimenters and poll-takers in all fields of statistical research. Supplies fundamental knowledge of virtually all elementary methods in use today by sociologists, psychologists, biologists, engineers, mathematicians, etc. Explains logical and mathematical basis of each method described, with examples for each section. Covers frequency distributions and measures, inference from random samples, errors in large samples, simple analysis of variance, multiple and partial regression and correlation, etc. 4th revised (1952) edition. 16 charts. 5 significance tables. 152-item bibliography. 96 tables. 22 figures. 395pp. 6 x 9.
S228 Clothbound **$7.50**

STATISTICS MANUAL, E. L. Crow, F. A. Davis, M. W. Maxfield. Comprehensive collection of classical, modern statistics methods, prepared under auspices of U. S. Naval Ordnance Test Station, China Lake, Calif. Many examples from ordnance will be valuable to workers in all fields. Emphasis is on use, with information on fiducial limits, sign tests, Chi-square runs, sensitivity, quality control, much more. "Well written . . . excellent reference work," Operations Research. Corrected edition of NAVORD Report 3360 NOTS 948. Introduction. Appendix of 32 tables, charts. Index. Bibliography. 95 illustrations. 306pp. 5⅜ x 8.
S599 Paperbound **$1.55**

ANALYSIS & DESIGN OF EXPERIMENTS, H. B. Mann. Offers a method for grasping the analysis of variance and variance design within a short time. Partial contents: Chi-square distribution and analysis of variance distribution, matrices, quadratic forms, likelihood ration tests and tests of linear hypotheses, power of analysis, Galois fields, non-orthogonal data, interblock estimates, etc. 15pp. of useful tables. x + 195pp. 5 x 7⅜. S180 Paperbound **$1.45**

Numerical analysis, tables

PRACTICAL ANALYSIS, GRAPHICAL AND NUMERICAL METHODS, F. A. Willers. Translated by R. T. Beyer. Immensely practical handbook for engineers, showing how to interpolate, use various methods of numerical differentiation and integration, determine the roots of a single algebraic equation, system of linear equations, use empirical formulas, integrate differential equations, etc. Hundreds of shortcuts for arriving at numerical solutions. Special section on American calculating machines, by T. W. Simpson. 132 illustrations. 422pp. 5⅜ x 8. S273 Paperbound **$2.00**

NUMERICAL SOLUTIONS OF DIFFERENTIAL EQUATIONS, H. Levy & E. A. Baggott. Comprehensive collection of methods for solving ordinary differential equations of first and higher order. All must pass 2 requirements: easy to grasp and practical, more rapid than school methods. Partial contents: graphical integration of differential equations, graphical methods for detailed solution. Numerical solution. Simultaneous equations and equations of 2nd and higher orders. "Should be in the hands of all in research in applied mathematics, teaching," NATURE. 21 figures. viii + 238pp. 5⅜ x 8. S168 Paperbound **$1.75**

NUMERICAL INTEGRATION OF DIFFERENTIAL EQUATIONS, Bennett, Milne & Bateman. Unabridged republication of original monograph prepared for National Research Council. New methods of integration of differential equations developed by 3 leading mathematicians: THE INTERPOLATIONAL POLYNOMIAL and SUCCESSIVE APPROXIMATIONS by A. A. Bennett; STEP-BY-STEP METHODS OF INTEGRATION by W. W. Milne; METHODS FOR PARTIAL DIFFERENTIAL EQUATIONS by H. Bateman. Methods for partial differential equations, transition from difference equations to differential equations, solution of differential equations to non-integral values of a parameter will interest mathematicians and physicists. 288 footnotes, mostly bibliographic; 235-item classified bibliography. 108pp. 5⅜ x 8. S305 Paperbound **$1.35**

INTRODUCTION TO RELAXATION METHODS, F. S. Shaw. Fluid mechanics, design of electrical networks, forces in structural frameworks, stress distribution, buckling, etc. Solve linear simultaneous equations, linear ordinary differential equations, partial differential equations, Eigen-value problems by relaxation methods. Detailed examples throughout. Special tables for dealing with awkwardly-shaped boundaries. Indexes. 253 diagrams. 72 tables. 400pp. 5⅜ x 8. S244 Paperbound **$2.45**

TABLES OF INDEFINITE INTEGRALS, G. Petit Bois. Comprehensive and accurate, this orderly grouping of over 2500 of the most useful indefinite integrals will save you hours of laborious mathematical groundwork. After a list of 49 common transformations of integral expressions, with a wide variety of examples, the book takes up algebraic functions, irrational monomials, products and quotients of binomials, transcendental functions, natural logs, etc. You will rarely or never encounter an integral of an algebraic or transcendental function not included here; any more comprehensive set of tables costs at least $12 or $15. Index. 2544 integrals. xii + 154pp. 6⅛ x 9¼. S225 Paperbound **$1.65**

A TABLE OF THE INCOMPLETE ELLIPTIC INTEGRAL OF THE THIRD KIND, R. G. Selfridge, J. E. Maxfield. The first complete 6 place tables of values of the incomplete integral of the third kind, prepared under the auspices of the Research Department of the U.S. Naval Ordnance Test Station. Calculated on an IBM type 704 calculator and thoroughly verified by echo-checking and a check integral at the completion of each value of **a.** Of inestimable value in problems where the surface area of geometrical bodies can only be expressed in terms of the incomplete integral of the third and lower kinds; problems in aero-, fluid-, and thermodynamics involving processes where nonsymmetrical repetitive volumes must be determined; various types of seismological problems; problems of magnetic potentials due to circular current; etc. Foreword. Acknowledgment. Introduction. Use of table. xiv + 805pp. 5⅝ x 8⅜. S501 Clothbound **$7.50**

MATHEMATICAL TABLES, H. B. Dwight. Unique for its coverage in one volume of almost every function of importance in applied mathematics, engineering, and the physical sciences. Three extremely fine tables of the three trig functions and their inverse functions to thousandths of radians; natural and common logarithms; squares, cubes; hyperbolic functions and the inverse hyperbolic functions; $(a^2 + b^2)$ exp. ½a; complete elliptic integrals of the 1st and 2nd kind; sine and cosine integrals; exponential integrals Ei(x) and Ei(−x); binomial coefficients; factorials to 250; surface zonal harmonics and first derivatives; Bernoulli and Euler numbers and their logs to base of 10; Gamma function; normal probability integral; over 60 pages of Bessel functions; the Riemann Zeta function. Each table with formulae generally used, sources of more extensive tables, interpolation data, etc. Over half have columns of differences, to facilitate interpolation. Introduction. Index. viii + 231pp. 5⅜ x 8. S445 Paperbound **$1.75**

PHYSICS

General physics

FOUNDATIONS OF PHYSICS, R. B. Lindsay & H. Margenau. Excellent bridge between semi-popular works & technical treatises. A discussion of methods of physical description, construction of theory; valuable for physicist with elementary calculus who is interested in ideas that give meaning to data, tools of modern physics. Contents include symbolism, mathematical equations; space & time foundations of mechanics; probability; physics & continua; electron theory; special & general relativity; quantum mechanics; causality. "Thorough and yet not overdetailed. Unreservedly recommended," NATURE (London). Unabridged, corrected edition. List of recommended readings. 35 illustrations. xi + 537pp. 5⅜ x 8.
S377 Paperbound **$2.45**

FUNDAMENTAL FORMULAS OF PHYSICS, ed. by D. H. Menzel. Highly useful, fully inexpensive reference and study text, ranging from simple to highly sophisticated operations. Mathematics integrated into text—each chapter stands as short textbook of field represented. Vol. 1: Statistics, Physical Constants, Special Theory of Relativity, Hydrodynamics, Aerodynamics, Boundary Value Problems in Math. Physics; Viscosity, Electromagnetic Theory, etc. Vol. 2: Sound, Acoustics, Geometrical Optics, Electron Optics, High-Energy Phenomena, Magnetism, Biophysics, much more. Index. Total of 800pp. 5⅜ x 8.
Vol. 1 S595 Paperbound **$2.00**
Vol. 2 S596 Paperbound **$2.00**

MATHEMATICAL PHYSICS, D. H. Menzel. Thorough one-volume treatment of the mathematical techniques vital for classic mechanics, electromagnetic theory, quantum theory, and relativity. Written by the Harvard Professor of Astrophysics for junior, senior, and graduate courses, it gives clear explanations of all those aspects of function theory, vectors, matrices, dyadics, tensors, partial differential equations, etc., necessary for the understanding of the various physical theories. Electron theory, relativity, and other topics seldom presented appear here in considerable detail. Scores of definitions, conversion factors, dimensional constants, etc. "More detailed than normal for an advanced text . . . excellent set of sections on Dyadics, Matrices, and Tensors," JOURNAL OF THE FRANKLIN INSTITUTE. Index. 193 problems, with answers. x + 412pp. 5⅜ x 8.
S56 Paperbound **$2.00**

THE SCIENTIFIC PAPERS OF J. WILLARD GIBBS. All the published papers of America's outstanding theoretical scientist (except for "Statistical Mechanics" and "Vector Analysis"). Vol I (thermodynamics) contains one of the most brilliant of all 19th-century scientific papers—the 300-page "On the Equilibrium of Heterogeneous Substances," which founded the science of physical chemistry, and clearly stated a number of highly important natural laws for the first time; 8 other papers complete the first volume. Vol II includes 2 papers on dynamics, 8 on vector analysis and multiple algebra, 5 on the electromagnetic theory of light, and 6 miscellaneous papers. Biographical sketch by H. A. Bumstead. Total of xxxvi + 718pp. 5⅝ x 8⅜.
S721 Vol I Paperbound **$2.00**
S722 Vol II Paperbound **$2.00**
The set **$4.00**

Dover publishes books on art, music, philosophy, literature, languages, history, social sciences, psychology, handcrafts, orientalia, puzzles and entertainments, chess, pets and gardens, books explaining science, intermediate and higher mathematics mathematical physics, engineering, biological sciences, earth sciences, classics of science, etc. Write to:

Dept. catrr.
Dover Publications, Inc.
180 Varick Street, N. Y. 14, N. Y.